the handbook of
Energy
drinks

the handbook of
Energy
drinks

Maria Costantino

Published by SILVERDALE BOOKS
An imprint of Bookmart Ltd
Registered number 2372865
Trading as Bookmart Ltd
Blaby Road
Wigston
Leicester LE18 4SE

© 2004 D&S Books Ltd

D&S Books Ltd
Kerswell,
Parkham Ash, Bideford
Devon, England
EX39 5PR

e-mail us at:-
enquiries@dsbooks.fsnet.co.uk

This edition printed 2004

ISBN 1-845090-65-9

DS0133. Handbook of Energy Drinks

Creative Director: Sarah King
Project editor: Sally MacEachern
Designer: Axis Design Editions
Photographer: Colin Bowling

Fonts used in this book: Sabon, Hack, Optima

Printed in China

1 3 5 7 9 10 8 6 4 2

Contents

Drinks for Health

All foods provide our body with energy, but some of these foods are better at it than others! Some enhance vitality, improve strength and stamina, and regenerate our bodies in marvellous ways. For decades, our parents and health practitioners have been telling us to eat more fruit and vegetables and to cut down on the fatty, sugary, salty and highly processed foods that have become part of our culture of eating in the west.

This fundamentally sensible advice has become increasingly supported by the growing interest in 'real foods', reflected in vitamin and mineral supplements, in the rise of health food stores, as well as in increasing numbers of books and magazines offering advice and plans for healthy eating. We know we should 'eat five' (portions of fruit and vegetables) each day, but most of us don't. Instead, we undermine the value of our food by eating too much of the wrong kinds and too little of the right kinds. In the USA for example, the average adult manages just one and half portions of fruit and vegetables a day; while in Britain a remarkable 65% of the population eat only one portion per day! No wonder we moan about being tired, run down, sick and lacking *joie de vivre*!

The recipes in this book are simple, quick, relatively inexpensive and effective ways of making sure you get at least some of the goodness from some of those 'five a day'. They're also delicious, will boost your energy considerably when you need it, relax you when it's time to wind down, and help keep your body in tip top condition.

The recipes are made of fruit and vegetables, and combinations of the two. Fruits and vegetables contain many of the vital minerals and vitamins that we need to stay healthy and fight off disease. By juicing fruits and vegetables, the raw nutrients – the vitamins, minerals, sugars, starches, and enzymes – form a pure concentration but without the fibrous plant cell walls. Juices are therefore absorbed quickly and easily by the body, without the trouble of digesting fibrous pulp. If you can't face eating a grapefruit in the morning, try juicing it instead. One grapefruit will on average yield 100 ml (3.5 fl oz) of glorious, vitamin and mineral packed juice.

Fruit and vegetable juices are a valuable part of a balanced diet, but are not 'complete' in themselves: juices lack fibre, fat and protein, which are also vital to maintain energy and preserve optimum health.

Why Fresh Juices?

Why, you might ask, do I have to go to the trouble of juicing a grapefruit or an orange when I can buy a carton of juice from my local supermarket? Pure, freshly squeezed or juiced fruit and vegetables allow you to enjoy the full flavour and contain nothing but pure juice. You can buy 'pure juices' in the stores but check the labels carefully: freshly squeezed or juiced products are likely to be in the chiller cabinet as they don't have any added preservatives and therefore have a short 'shelf life'. Pure juices are also not based on juice concentrates, which are evaporated and then re-diluted, a process in which they can lose many of their essential nutriments as well as some of their flavour and aroma.

Beware cartons and bottles that say 'juice drink' or 'nectar' as such drinks may contain as little as 5% juice and have added sweeteners, acids and flavour enhancers to make up for the lack of fruits! As with fruits, vegetable juices such as tomato and carrot can be pure, made from concentrates, or diluted and with additives – so read those labels!

If you don't want to juice your own, many natural and whole food stores can provide you with the real thing – but often only in a limited variety. Orange and other citrus juices will be stocked, as well as apple and berry juices, often in small amounts. But you may find that some pure fruits and many pure vegetable juices are just not to be found. So why deny yourself the pleasures and benefits of freshly juiced mangoes, kiwis or apricots, of carrots and even the surprisingly sweet taste of beetroot!

Juicy fresh produce ensures nothing but pure juice and full flavour.

Squeezing, juicing and pureeing

Whole, raw fruits and vegetables juiced at home contain more of the essential, life-giving and health enhancing nutriments than the juices you buy in the stores. This is because commercial juices are normally pasteurised to prolong their shelf life.

Fresh citrus fruit – oranges, lemons, grapefruits – squeezed from the whole fruit and enjoyed immediately will have more of those nutrients. You can simply squeeze these fruits using a reamer, or you can peel the fruits and pop them whole into a liquidizer/food processor and 'whiz' them into juice. If you want, you can press or strain the puree through a fine sieve to remove the fruit pulp and any large seeds. Or you can blend the whole puree – pulp and all – with another juice.

'Watery' fruits like melons and cucumbers as well as soft fruits like berries, apricots, kiwis, melons and tomatoes can also be 'juiced' in the same way: if you ever

Many of the recipes used in this book can be made using a food processor.

wondered what all those 'bits' were that came attached to your food processor, you might be surprised to find that you have a blade for juice extraction that works in the same way as a centrifugal juicer already at your finger tips

Juicers: centrifuge or masticator?

Before you rush out to buy the latest state-of-the-art juicing monster that is most suited to a restaurant or juice bar, think exactly what your needs are: budget, the size of your kitchen, for individual or family use, speed and volume, and finally, centrifuge or masticator! Don't be alarmed! There are two types of juicing machines generally on offer- with prices ranging from the very affordable to those that induce a shocked 'you're kidding!' response when you see the price tag!

As in all things in life, you get what you pay for. The more efficient masticating machines literally pulverize fruit and vegetables by pushing them through wire mesh with such force that the juice is separated from the pulp – even in the apparently 'driest' of veggies like parsnips and turnips. Because masticating juicers can extract larger amounts of juice from fruits and veggies, the juices made with these have more nutrients in them. Masticating machines are generally on the large size, and have slowly rotating cutters that incorporate less oxygen so the juice made in these will last for up to 24 hours if refrigerated.

Centrifugal juicers work by finely chopping and grating the produce and spinning it round at speed so that

Centrifugal juice extractors are ideal for home use.

centrifugal force pushes it through a wire mesh separating the pulp from the juice.

They are less powerful machines – ideally suited to the home market – but a little less efficient at extracting all the goodness of the produce. Juicing purists claim that unlike a masticator, a centrifugal juice instantly exposes the juice to oxygen – which makes it deteriorate – so juices made in these need to be drunk immediately. Most people find though, that whatever their machine, juice stored in a sealed container in a fridge at around 2–4 degrees C (35–38 degrees F) will keep for up to one day.

Useful gizmos

Some of the recipes in this book can be made with a blender, but some will require a juicer. Start with what you've got, then when you are 'hooked' add a juicer to your birthday gift 'wish list' and let your friends and family know! In addition, most gadgets and gizmos are probably already in your kitchen cupboards. **Weighing scales** are useful for when you

need to keep an eye on quantities. The 'Food Facts' section dealing with different fruits and vegetables will give you an approximate guide to the amount of juice you can expect from them, but do remember, the yield will depend also on your juicer, and the size and quality of the fruit and veggies you use: one person's idea of 'small' is another person's 'enormous'!

Scrubbing brushes are needed to clean fruit and veggies before cutting them and juicing them. Always wash fruit and vegetables before cutting them and juicing them. A small brush – a toothbrush is ideal – or a bottle brush are great for cleaning out those hard to get at corners in your juicer.

Knives/peelers are already in your kitchen. Some fruits and veggies need to be peeled before juicing – especially non-organic produce – and some, like the lovely kiwi, may cause allergic reactions. In the section on 'food facts' where there is a possible 'risk' of allergic reaction, this is indicated.

Chopping board. Some fruit and vegetables will have to be chopped up to fit into your juicer/blender – there's no way you'll get a whole melon in a domestic juicer!

Graters/choppers.
Again they're probably already in your kitchen. Use the grater for grating spices like ginger and nutmeg, and choppers for herbs.

Measuring jug. You'll need this to help you mix the juices in the 'right' quantities – at least to begin with. As you become more familiar with juicing different fruits and vegetables, you'll be able to gauge by eye! You can also use the measuring jug as a mixing jug: juice each fruit or vegetable separately and then combine them in the jug before pouring into a glass.

Storage bottle/container. Freshly juiced fruits and vegetables will not store for long periods even when refrigerated. Once they are exposed to the air, the juices will start their process of 'decomposing'. It is possible only to slow down this process by storing juice in an airtight bottle in the fridge at around 2–4 degrees C (35–38 degrees F). This should 'keep' for up to one day and allow it to remain as tasty as when you first juiced it. However, don't make huge quantities of juice unless you can guarantee you are going to drink it. Fresh juices, even with refrigeration, will oxidise and go off – which is a waste of produce, time and energy!

Glasses. Whatever you do, don't take slugs of juice direct from the storage bottle! You'll end up transferring some of your body's primary digestive enzyme – saliva – into the juice and it will start digesting it in the bottle! When we go out to a restaurant or bar, food and drink always tastes and looks so nice, it's hard to resist it! A large part of the satisfaction we get from dining out is from the 'look' of food: get the same satisfaction at home by using an attractive glass for your juices and take a moment to demonstrate your artistry with an attractive garnish too.

A simple slice of lemon, orange, or kiwi, a sprig of mint or lemon balm, a sprinkling of herbs or a bunch of fresh leaves will please the eye and boost the appetite. Add a straw, a swizzle stick – or an edible swizzle stick in the form of a stick of cucumber, carrot or celery – or drop in an ice cube or two. One of the nicest surprises in a cool drink on a hot summer day is to discover the ice cubes are made of apple or grape juice and that there's even a grape, a blueberry or a strawberry frozen inside it!

How much juice?

Remember: enjoy juices as part of a balanced diet. Juicing removes the fibre from fruit and vegetables and juices alone cannot provide the complete range of nutritional needs for the body: we all need a balance of fats, carbohydrates and proteins for our bodies to function completely and to maintain health. While fruit juices are very tasty, it is important that we drink equal amounts of vegetable drinks otherwise we would be consuming far too much sugar, which is present as fructose in all fruits.

The key to juicing your way to energy and vitality is of course moderation. Two glasses of freshly juiced fruits and vegetables is enough: nutritionists advise beginners not to exceed more than 3 x 225 ml (8 fl oz) glasses of fresh juice a day. Vegetables juiced can be a good way of getting kids to 'eat their greens', but limit their intake to 150 ml (5 fl oz) per day. Try offering them small 'shot' glasses of juice which can be fun to drink – and will get them used to the flavour. Dilute 'longer' drinks with mineral water.

Dark green vegetables such as spinach and broccoli, and dark red vegetables like beetroot, are strong and are an acquired taste. These are best mixed in a ration of 1 part dark green juice to 4 parts carrot, apple or even cucumber juice, to 'smooth' them out. Carrot and apple juice are great in that they mix well with everything: generally, fruit and vegetable juices when mixed can cause flatulence!

Food Facts

The energy boosting and medicinal properties of foods have been acknowledged for thousands of years and modern scientific research has found hundreds of beneficial nutrients in the foods we eat. By applying this knowledge of the nutrients available in the 'food pharmacy' and how they work, we can 'get the most' out of what we eat.

Food Facts – Fruit

Fruit is one of the easiest and most delicious ways to boost energy and increase the number and amount of nutrients.

Citrus fruits

The main providers of Vitamin C, citrus fruits include oranges, lemons, limes, grapefruits, and mandarins – which also include tangerines, satsumas and clementines.

Oranges

This subtropical orange-coloured citrus fruit is botanically, a berry! There are two types of oranges – the sweet, or China, orange which indicates its origins, and, the bitter or Seville orange, which is primarily used in making marmalade and the famous orange-flavoured liqueurs such as Grand Marnier. The orange travelled from the east along the spice route to India where its Sanskrit name was *nagaranga* which eventually became the Arabic *narang*. The Portuguese took them to the Americas and they found their way to their colonies in South America: today, Brazil is the single largest producer of fruits for juice.

Famed for their high Vitamin C content, oranges also contain potassium and some calcium. The pith is also an exceptionally good source of bioflavinoids (Vitamin P) which strengthen the walls of the tiny blood capillaries: in scurvy, these walls collapse and the skin shows tiny haemorrhages all over the body! Navel oranges – which are

Note

The yields of juice for fruits and vegetables given are approximate guides only. If you are ill, have or suspect you may have an allergy or food intolerance, you need to consult a doctor. The recipes suggested are NOT substitutes for medical advice or prescribed medicines.

identifiable by the bellybutton-like spot at their blossom end – are seedless oranges native to Brazil and have a thick, easy to peel skin. Valencia oranges have numerous pips but juicy sweet flesh and are great for juicing. From southern Spain and Italy come the gorgeous sweet blood oranges with their red-orange flesh. The fruit, flower and peel of oranges has long been used in traditional remedies: the peel contains heseperidine and limonene, which is used in the treatment of chronic bronchitis. Jupiter is said to have given Juno an orange on their wedding day, and so fragrant is the blossom that many modern brides still have it in their wedding bouquets.

Nutrients and active ingredients: Vitamins A, B6, C, thiamine, folic acid, magnesium, potassium, phosphorous, iron, riboflavin, protein, sugars.

Beneficial properties: Antioxidant, anti-stress, lowers cholesterol, increases iron absorption.

Calorific values (per standard portion): approx. 59 KCal.

Quantity/number required to make 100 ml (3 ½ fl oz): 2.

Preparation: Peel and quarter.

Warning !

Some migraine sufferers may be sensitive to one or all citrus fruits. It is advisable to avoid oranges if you suffer from rheumatoid arthritis. All citrus fruits – especially lemons – consumed in excess can deplete the body's reserves – the bones and teeth – of calcium.

Lemons

A native of northern India, the lemon gets its name from the Hindustani word *limu*. The sharp taste of lemons is because they have less sugar and more citric acid than oranges – which is why sucking a lemon is unpleasant – and the high acid content can be erosive on the teeth! But lemons are one of the most effective remedies for treating colds and flu, as well as indigestion. Lemon helps protect the mucus membrane lining of the digestive tract and is said to be a stimulant for the liver and pancreas. Its antibacterial qualities make lemons a traditional choice for sore throats when the juice is well diluted with hot water – and a spoon of honey – but a dab of lemon juice on a spot can 'dry' it up! In the shops you are most likely to find the two main varieties of lemon: in winter, the smooth-skinned Lisbon, which has a long nipple at the blossom end, in summer, the more rounded Eureka.

Nutrients and active ingredients: Vitamins C, some B, E, potassium, magnesium, calcium, phosphorous, copper, zinc, iron, manganese, bioflavinoids, limonene and mucilage.

Beneficial properties: Antibacterial, antioxidant, antiallergic; lowers blood-fat levels and helps to maintain the health of the heart, nerves and muscle tissue.

Calorific values: 22 KCal per 100 g.

Quantity/number required to make 100 ml (3 ½ fl oz): 3.

Preparation: Peel and quarter.

Limes

The smallest of the citrus fruits, limes also have the most fragile shelf lives because of their thin skins. Grown in the tropics from Egypt to the West Indies, limes are the most acidic of all the citrus fruits and although they have more vitamin C than a grapefruit, they have less than oranges and lemons. They are the most gorgeous colour, the juice imparts flavour to other ingredients and the smell is wonderful.

Nutrients and active ingredients: Vitamin C, folate, calcium, potassium, citric acid, fibre, bioflavinoids.
Beneficial properties: Antioxidant, antibacterial.
Calorific values: 20 KCal per 100g.
Quantity/number required to make 100 ml (3 ½ fl oz): 3.
Preparation: Peel and break into segments and feed into juicer.

Grapefruits

The largest member of the citrus family is named not because of its taste but because its fruits are borne in clusters, resembling a bunch of grapes! It is one of the most important citrus fruits to have originated outside of Asia: hybridised in Jamaica in the West Indies the grapefruit was possibly a hybrid between the pommelo and sweet orange. It has been cultivated commercially in the New World for just over 100 years. The two types are ruby and white: rubies have pink flesh and a pinkish blush to their yellow skin. Rubies are generally sweeter – and are higher in Vitamin C – than whites. A popular 'slimmer's food', grapefruit is an 'eliminator' – a powerful detoxifier, stimulating the liver.

Nutrients and active ingredients: Vitamins A, C, folate, potassium, bioflavinoids, citric and phenolic acids, fibre, pectin, sugars.
Beneficial properties: Antioxidant, anticancer, antimicrobal, lowers blood pressure, lowers cholesterol, stimulates the digestive system, stimulates the immune system, detoxing.
Calorific values: 32 KCal per 100g.
Quantity/number required to make 100 ml (3 ½ fl oz): 1.
Preparation: Peel and break into segments.

Mandarins

The mandarin 'family' – of which satsumas, the Mediterranean mandarin and the common mandarin – are the main hybrids. Common mandarins include clementines, tangors (which are a hybrid of mandarins and oranges!) and tangelos (a hybrid of the mandarin, grapefruit and pommelo!) Mandarins – and all their sweet relatives – are less acidic than grapefruits or lemons and are still good sources of Vitamin C and folate, although they contain less potassium and fewer of the B vitamins.

Nutrients and active ingredients: Vitamins C, B1 (thiamine), potassium, folate.
Beneficial properties: Antioxidant, anticancer, lowers cholesterol, circulation improvers, good for sore throats.
Calorific values: 35 KCal per 100g.
Quantity/number required to make 100 ml (3 ½ fl oz): 3.
Preparation: Peel and break into segments

Warning !

Some migraine sufferers may be sensitive to one or all citrus fruits. It is advisable to avoid oranges if you suffer from rheumatoid arthritis. All citrus fruits – especially lemons – consumed in excess can deplete the body's reserves – the bones and teeth – of calcium.

Pome Fruits

Pome fruits include apples, pears and quinces.

Apples

Apples are the world's most popular temperate zone fruit. There are more than 7,000 varieties but the 'parent' of them all is the humble, and barely edible, crab apple (*Malus sylvestris*)! Traditionally apples have been used for treating stomach upsets: a little grated apple left to turn brown and mixed with a little honey is a very effective remedy for diarrhoea. At the other end of the scale, their soluble fibre is a vital weapon in relieving constipation! The very smell of an apple has been shown to have a calming effect on the nervous system and helps to lower blood pressure. The sugar in apples is mostly fructose, which is broken down and releases its energy slowly: this helps to keep blood sugar levels on an even keel. Apples are also said to help relieve the symptoms of a hangover!

Nutrients and active ingredients: Vitamin C, potassium, malic acid, tannin, fibre, pectin, sugars.
Beneficial properties: Lowers cholesterol, lowers blood pressure, detoxifying, aids the digestive system.
Calorific values: 47 Kcal per average apple.
Quantity/number required to make 100 ml (3 ½ fl oz): 2.
Preparation: Wash and chop to fit feeder of juicer. No need to peel or core.

Pears

When fully ripe, pears are so soft many people call them 'butter fruits'. Unlike most tree fruits, pears ripen best off the tree! The records of the Renaissance Grand Duke Cosimo III de Medici showed his passion for pears: 209 different varieties were served at his table in one year! All too often we think of pears as a sweet dessert fruit and overlook their nutritional values: a good source of soluble pectin, which is a bowel regulator, they don't just lower cholesterol, they actually eliminate it from the body! A reasonable source of Vitamin C, they also have Vitamin A, potassium and a little E, but it's their soluble fibre that is the real winner – a much tastier alternative to bran!

Nutrients and active ingredients: Vitamins C, A, E, potassium, fibre.
Beneficial properties: Good for energy and recovery after illness, good for the digestive system, cholesterol lowering.
Calorific values: 64 KCal per average pear.
Quantity/number required to make 100 ml (3 ½ fl oz): 2.
Preparation: Wash and chop – no need to peel or core.

Warning !

Fresh pears contain a sugar-based alcohol called sorbitol. This sugar free sweetener is used in many 'tooth friendly' foods and toothpaste but it may cause diarrhoea in some susceptible folk.

Stone Fruits

Apricots

The name of this golden fruit is derived from the Latin *praecoquum*, which means 'early ripe'. The English called it the 'hastie peche' because it was one of the first fresh fruits to appear in summer. Apricots are botanically related to nectarines and peaches, but each has its own uniquely delicious flavour. They are also related to almonds – look closely at the almond shaped stone! Originating in China, where they were reputed to have medicinal properties benefiting the heart, apricots found their way to Europe then on to North and South America. High in Vitamin A and containing several minerals they are good sources of carbohydrates and are low in fat. In recipes calling for apricots, you can substitute nectarines or peaches, or even dried fruits, but 'rehydrate' them first, either by soaking in cold water for an hour or cooking in a little water over a low heat until soft and plump. Then drain of the liquor and use the fruits as if fresh.

Nutrients and active ingredients: Vitamins A, B2, B3, B5, carotene, calcium, magnesium, potassium, copper, iron, zinc, fibre, sugar. (Dried apricots are also a rich source of iron).
Beneficial properties: Antioxidant, stimulates the immune system by encouraging antibody production, detoxifying, helps stabilise blood sugars, helps the release of energy from food and stored tissues, enhances the transport of

oxygen in the blood.

Calorific values: Fresh: 30 KCal per 100g (3 ½ oz). Dried: 190 KCal per 100g).

Quantity/number required to make 100 ml: (3 ½ fl oz) 6 fresh, 4–5 dried, rehydrated.

Preparation: Wash fresh fruit and remove stone. Rehydrate dried fruits.

Warning !

Dried fruits that have been treated with sulphur dioxide should be avoided as this can trigger asthma attacks.

Peaches and Nectarines

The drink of the Greek gods was *nektar*, hence the name of this lovely fruit. It has been known since ancient times, but was often mistaken for a recent hybrid of peaches and plums. However, a nectarine is not a 'shaved peach' – nor is a peach a 'fuzzy' nectarine! But nutritionally there is little between the nectarine and the 'Persian plum' or peach whose botanical name is *persica* because early scientists believed it had originated in Persia and not, as we now know, in China. Today about half of the world's production of peaches and nectarines is supplied by Italy and the USA. They are usually described as 'clingstone' (when the flesh of the fruit clings to the stone – these are usually sold canned) or 'freestone' (when the flesh is easily removed from the stone).

Nutrients and active ingredients: Vitamin C, betacarotene, some fibre, folic acid, potassium, phosphorous.

Beneficial properties: Antioxidant; good for the digestive system: a gentle laxative, virtually fat and sodium free: ideal for those with high cholesterol and blood pressure problems; believed to benefit the nervous system and help prevent degenerative disease.

Calorific values: Nectarine 60 Kcal per 100g (3 ½ oz). Peach 36 KCal per 100g.

Quantity/number required to make 100 ml (3 ½ fl oz): 2.

Preparation: Wash and remove stone.

Cherries

Related to peaches and plums, cherries are one of the few fruits that are available for all 12 months of the year, so we can enjoy their taste and benefits all the time. The parent of all cherries – whether the sweet eating cherry or the sour 'pie' cherry – is the choke cherry, a bitter, astringent fruit that is smaller than the 'stone' in a 'normal' cherry. An ancient fruit, its traces have been found in Stone Age sites in Europe and America. The 'modern' sweet cheery probably began life in pre-biblical times in the orchards of Mesopotamia and they were valued by ancient physicians for their cleansing and 'rejuvenating' properties. They are good detoxers and a mild laxative; they soothe the nervous system and can help relieve stress. But it is their content of ellagic acid, which inhibits the growth of cancerous cells, that makes these little juicy fruits valuable in the fight against cancers.

Nutrients and active ingredients: Vitamins C, A, bioflavinoids, ellagic acid, phosphorous, potassium and calcium plus minimal amounts of B-complex vitamins (B2, folic acid).
Beneficial properties: Antioxidant, anticancer, diuretic; low sodium; beneficial to the nervous system; stress-reliever; mildly laxative.
Calorific values: 47 KCal per 100g (3 ½ oz).
Quantity/number required to make 100 ml (3 ½ fl oz): 150-200 g (5–7 oz).
Preparation: Wash, de-stalk and remove stones.

Plums

Plums are cousins of peaches and cherries – and thousands of varieties can be found growing on every continent except Antarctica! The 20 or so commercial varieties available are classified as European or Japanese/Asian. The European plums have purple or blue skins and are small and firm. The Japanese varieties are generally larger and juicier and are red, yellow or green. Plums are widely used in oriental medicine, especially the Japanese Umiboshi, to treat digestive disorders.

Nutrients and active ingredients: A little Vitamin C, modest amounts of Vitamin A and some Vitamin E, folic acid, betacarotene, good source of potassium; when dried as prunes, they are excellent sources of iron, Vitamin A, potassium, calcium and magnesium.
Beneficial properties: Good for the heart and circulation; good for the digestive system (gently laxative, especially dried as prunes); diuretic.
Calorific values: 40 KCal per 100g.
Quantity/number required to make 100 ml (3 ½ fl oz): 4-6 depending on size.
Preparation: Wash and remove stone.

Warning !

Dried plums (prunes) and all dried fruits that have been treated with sulphur dioxide should be avoided as this can trigger asthma attacks.

Avocados

Sometimes called an avocado pear, this fruit started life in Peru some 9,000 years ago. Indigenous natives of South America have for centuries been using the fruit, dried and fresh leaves, rind, bark, flesh and even the stone or seed as medicine. The flesh and oil have long been popular to treat skin ailments and we now know that the Vitamin E contained in it stimulates the production of collagen, which helps smooth out wrinkles – and it's cheaper and more pleasant than a face lift! It's also a high-protein, high-energy and high-protection factor food containing anti-fungal and antibacterial chemicals. The mono-unsaturated fats – especially oleic acid – make avocados one of the most powerful antioxidant foods known to man – and woman – and offer protection against heart diseases, strokes and cancers. The B6 helps iron out mood swings, making avocados very useful for PMS sufferers.

Nutrients and active ingredients: Vitamins E, K, B1, B2, B3, B5, biotin, folate, potassium, zinc, carotenoids, fibre, unsaturated fatty acids, including oleic acid
Beneficial properties: Anticancer, anti-fungal, antioxidant.

Warning !

If you are allergic to natural rubber (latex) you have a 50-50 chance of being allergic to avocados.

Calorific values: 225 KCal per 100g.
Quantity/number required to make 100 ml (3 ½ fl oz): n/a, best made into smoothies!
Preparation: Cut in half, remove the stone and scoop the flesh out.

Melons

Melons are members of the gourd family of vegetables, which includes cucumbers, pumpkins and marrows – except watermelons, which are botanically unrelated to melons. Melons have been cultivated in Asia since the most ancient times and were valued as fruits by the ancient Egyptians, Greeks and Romans but were only introduced to Europe in the late 16th century when they were first cultivated by the French. Cooling and delicious in summer, all forms of melon are stimulating to the kidneys and gently laxative. Cantaloupe melons are particularly valuable in the 'food pharmacy': they increase the release of energy from other foods and have a high level of carotenoids, which may inhibit the growth of cancer cells

Nutrients and active ingredients: Cantaloupe: Vitamins A, C, B3, carotenoids. Watermelons: Vitamin B5.
Beneficial properties: Cantaloupe: Antioxidant, anticancer, laxative, diuretic, low sodium. Watermelons: Energy metabolisers, diuretic, laxative, low sodium.
Calorific values: Cantaloupe: 30 KCal per 100g. Watermelon: 62 KCal per 100g.
Quantity/number required to make 100 ml (½ fl oz): Cantaloupe: and Watermelon: one good sized slice about 4–5 cm (2–3 in) thick.
Preparation: Remove pips and skin if desired.

Grapes

The beginnings of the grape are lost in the mists of time; for millennia grapes have been used for the production of wine and raisins. The 'parent' species of most modern grape production is *Vitis vinifera,* which was taken to the New World by Columbus. Nourishing, strengthening, refreshing and cleansing, it no surprise that we take grapes as gifts to sick friends in hospital: they are excellent for convalescents and their nutritive values were confirmed by Mahatma Gandhi, who drank grape juice during his extended fasts. Grapes contain far more aromatic compounds than any other fruit: astringent tannins, flavones, linanol, nerol, geraniol among them, which are believed to have anticancer properties.

Nutrients and active ingredients: Vitamins B3, B6, E, biotin, magnesium, phosphorous, copper, iron, selenium, zinc.
Beneficial properties: Anti-inflammatory, antioxidant, anticancer, detoxifying, diuretic.
Calorific values: 60 KCal per 100g.
Quantity/number required to make 100 ml (3 ½ fl oz): about 150g (50z) fruits.
Preparation: Wash thoroughly and remove stalks.

Warning !

Since most grapes are sprayed during cultivation, careful washing is vital prior to ingestion.

Berry Fruits

Berries are fruits that seem to cause delight: they always seem just right for popping into the mouth and enjoying! Hundreds of wild fruits are called berries but only about ten have been domesticated and cultivated and are much larger than their wild cousins. Because they are an energy and labour intensive crop, berries are generally more expensive pound for pound than other fruits, but these little fruits are packed with vitamins and minerals.

Strawberries

Until the 1660s, the only strawberries available in Europe were the tiny but juicy wild variety. Originally alpines – some of these are still grown today by keen gardeners for their superior flavour – the majority of the berries we eat today are descended from two American varieties that were brought to Europe from Virginia in the early 17th and late 18th centuries. Linneaus, the great Swedish botanist, recommended strawberries as a cure for arthritis, gout and rheumatism–– chronic ailments from which he suffered. It seems that the berries help to eliminate uric acid from the body.

Nutrients and active ingredients: Vitamins C, B3, B5, iron, soluble fibre, pectin.

Beneficial properties: Reputed to reduce high blood pressure, helps in elimination of uric acid and kidney stones, helps prevent and treat anaemia and fatigue, lowers cholesterol, anti-viral properties, astringent, diuretic and mildly laxative.

Calorific values: 30 KCal per 100g.

Quantity/number required to make 100 ml (3 ½ fl oz): 200g (7 oz).

Preparation: Wash, then hull – don't wash when the hulls have been removed because the berries then get waterlogged!

Warning !

Some people may be sensitive to strawberries and have allergic reactions, which in some instances may be extreme, even life-threatening.

Blueberries

Blueberry, bilberry, whortleberry, huckleberry or whinberry, this gorgeous berry – not too sweet and not too sour – is native to both North America and Europe.

They have a fair amount of Vitamin C and small amounts of B1, betacarotene and potassium, but it is their antibacterial anthocyanosides that are valued in strengthening the walls of blood vessels, and in the treatment of cystitis and other urinary infections.

Nutrients and active ingredients: Vitamins C, B1, betacarotene, potassium, anthocyanosides, fibre.

Beneficial properties: Antibacterial, antioxidant, antiseptic, anti-inflammatory, toning effect on the blood vessels.

Calorific values: 30 KCal per 100g.

Quantity/number required to make 100 ml (3 ½ fl oz): 200 g (7 oz).

Preparation: Wash carefully.

Blackberries

Wild blackberries, or brambles, are an ancient fruit mentioned in the Bible. The ancient Greeks recommended them for treating gout. Each tiny bump on a blackberry – or raspberry – is in fact a tiny fruit called a drupelet. Blackberries and raspberries are not therefore 'true' berries, but magnificent little clusters of drupelets! The wild berries are richer in Vitamin E than their cultivated cousins, so it's worthwhile – and fun – picking your own! The high vitamin C content makes them a valuable antioxidant, protecting against diseases and infections.

Nutrients and active ingredients: Vitamins C, E, B3, folate, manganese, iron, potassium, citric acid, soluble fibre.

Beneficial properties: Antioxidant, toning, good for the heart, circulation and skin; good for colds and flu recovery.

Calorific values: 25 KCal per 100g.

Quantity/number required to make 100 ml (3 ½ fl oz): 200 g (7 oz).

Preparation: Wash carefully.

Raspberries

Like blackberries, raspberries are in fact clusters of tiny individual fruits called drupelets. When you pop a raspberry into your mouth, you are in fact eating about 80 single little fruits at a time! Their nutrients make them ideal foods for convalescents and those recovering from colds and flu, as well as those with heart problems, fatigue, and depression. A high Vitamin C content means that for 100g you'll get 75% of your recommended daily allowance. When you feel down, pop a raspberry in your mouth and boost your body and spirit!

Nutrients and active ingredients: Vitamins C, B3, biotin, folate, manganese, iron, citric acid, fibre.
Beneficial properties: Antioxidant, detoxifying, toning, good for gum disease, upset stomachs and diarrhoea.
Calorific values: 15 KCal per 100g.
Quantity/number required to make 100 ml (3 ½ fl oz): 200 g (7 oz).
Preparation: Wash carefully.

Blackcurrants

These berries are an exceptionally rich source of Vitamin C, which has traditionally made them the fruit of choice for fighting off colds and flu. The anthocyanosides – the pigments in their purple-black skin – are antibacterial and anti-inflammatory – which is why these berries have long been used to soothe sore throats.

Nutrients and active ingredients: Vitamin C, anthocyanosides, potassium.
Beneficial properties: Anti-inflammatory, antibacterial, immune boosting; good for recovery from colds and flu; anticancer, diuretic, stress buster, helps lower blood pressure.
Calorific values: 28 KCal per 100 g.
Quantity/number required to make 100 ml (3 1/2 fl oz): 200 g (7 oz).
Preparation: Wash carefully

Cranberries

To my knowledge, this relative of the blueberry is the only fruit required to do the high jump! During preparation for marketing, cranberries are sorted and graded by a bouncing test: the berries are required to bounce over 4–7 inch barriers. Those that make it get a gold medal and end up in the stores; those that don't bounce are too soft and are sent back to the locker room! Cranberries are also one of the few fruits native to North America; for centuries Native North Americans used them as both food and medicine, especially for bathing wounds and drawing out poisons from arrow injuries. Thanks to the berries' high Vitamin C content, American settlers were able to avoid the terrors of scurvy, and while English ships carried limes (hence 'Limeys') American whalers carried barrels of cranberries. The most popular 'medicinal' use of the berries today is in the treatment and prevention of cystitis: the juice prevents the bacteria from sticking to the bladder wall.

Nutrients and active ingredients: Vitamin C, iron, anthocyanosides, benzoic, citric and quinic acids, fibre.
Beneficial properties: Immune boosting; antibacterial: good for cystitis and urinary infections.
Calorific values: 11 KCal per 100g.
Quantity/number required to make 100 ml (3 ½ fl oz): 200 g (7 oz).
Preparation: Wash carefully – only before using though!

Tropical and Exotic Fruits

Once the preserve of the very rich, today we are indeed fortunate that we can enjoy a huge variety of fruits that are not native to our own countries. Supermarkets, greengrocers and market stalls not only provide apples and oranges but persimmons, pomegranates, kumquats and carambolas (star fruits) to serve the tastes of our multicultural communities. If you've never tasted a guava or a passion fruit, now's your chance!

Kiwis

'An emerald in a fur coat' is a nice way to describe this native of China (which is why it's also known as the Chinese Gooseberry) now grown in New Zealand and named after the nation's emblem, the kiwi bird. It is indeed a rich fruit: twice as much vitamin C as an orange and more fibre than an apple! Rich too in potassium – lack of this vital mineral can lead to high blood pressure, depression, chronic fatigue and poor digestion – it also contains an enzyme called actinidin, which is similar in action to the papain found in papaya.

Nutrients and active ingredients: Vitamins A, C, B3, fibre, potassium, actinidin.
Beneficial properties: Antioxidant, immune boosting, good for the skin and digestive system, gentle laxative.
Calorific values: about 30 KCal in an average fruit.
**Quantity/number required to make 100 ml (3

½ fl oz): 3.
Preparation: Peel off skin.

Warning !
Some people may be sensitive to the furry skin: avoid contact with the mouth.

Papaya (Paw Paw)
This beauty was a native of Costa Rica and Southern Mexico. It was called a 'tree melon' by Columbus and can weigh between 1 and 20 lb.! Thanks to the Spanish who introduced the fruit to Manila in the mid-16th century, papayas are now grown throughout the tropics. The world's largest producer today is the USA, with most of the fruits grown in Hawaii. This is a vital foodstuff in the developing world for the lovely papaya bears fruit all year round. It is also full of Vitamin C and an excellent source of betacarotene, which the body then converts into Vitamin A. The digestive enzyme papain is also valuable: this is extracted for commercial use in toothpaste, chewing gum and as a meat tenderiser! The seeds, though bitter, are edible – they look a bit like caviar!

Nutrients and active ingredients: Vitamin C, betacarotene, fibre, papain, potassium, phosphorous.
Beneficial properties: Antiallergic, antibacterial, antioxidant, detoxer; boosting: good for the digestive system, beneficial for the skin and eyes.
Calorific values: 50 KCal per standard fruit.
Quantity/number required to make 100 ml (3 ½ fl oz): 1.
Preparation: Cut in half, scoop out seeds, and remove flesh from skin.

Mango

Cultivated and eaten for more than 4,000 years in its native India, where Ayurvedic medicine used the fruit to treat high blood pressure and diabetes, the mango has now spread to China, the Philippines, the Mediterranean, Africa, Central, South and North America. Positively bursting with goodies, one mango will provide you with a day's Vitamin C, two-thirds of your Vitamin A, half your Vitamin E, a quarter of your fibre needs, and a cocktail of potassium, iron and nictinic acid working as antioxidants and papain, the protein-digesting enzyme. And they are absolutely delicious too!

Nutrients and active ingredients: Vitamins A, C, E, B3, potassium, iron, nictinic acid, papain, fibre.
Beneficial properties: Antibacterial, anticancer, antioxidant, energy boosting, immune system booster, detoxifier.
Calorific values: 86 KCal per standard fruit.
Quantity/number required to make 100 ml (3 ½ fl oz): 1 good sized fruit.
Preparation: Cut in half, remove stone and scoop flesh from skin.

Warning !

The peel of mangoes, especially when fully ripe, can be an irritant. The fruit belongs to the same family as poison ivy and anyone sensitized by contact with this, or mangoes, may suffer a severe reaction as excessive handling can irritate.

Passion Fruit

Also known as granadilla, this purple fruit the shape and size of a large egg gets its name from the Passion of Christ: the 12 white petals are the Apostles, the red stamens are the wounds, the nails and crown of thorns are the disc floret. The sweet golden flesh has a punchy flavour and many black, edible seeds that cannot be separated from the flesh unless strained. But you can eat it like a melon, puree it or turn it into juice: whichever way you use one, it's delicious and will boost your energy levels, lift your spirits and help ensure healthy skin and nerves.

Nutrients and active ingredients: Vitamins A, C, B2, B3, magnesium, phosphorous, iron, zinc, fibre.
Beneficial properties: Anti-allergy, anticancer, antioxidant, energy boosting.
Calorific values: 90 KCal per average fruit.
Quantity/number required to make 100 ml (3 ½ fl oz): 3.
Preparation: Passion fruits are 'ripe' when the smooth skin becomes wrinkled and the contents sound liquid when you shake the fruit! Cut in half and scoop out the flesh and seeds.

Pineapple

The only fruit to co-star with Elvis Presley, the pineapple is in fact native to South America and is not a fruit in the ordinary sense of the word: it is in fact a multiple organ that forms when the fruits of around a hundred or so flowers coalesce! The juice of fresh pineapple is an effective remedy for sore throats but its most valuable ingredient is an enzyme called bromelain, which can digest many times its own weight of protein in a few minutes: the enzyme only breaks down food and dead tissue, leaving our own intestines intact! It has also been found to be valuable in breaking down blood clots and so makes excellent health insurance for the heart!

Nutrients and active ingredients: Vitamins A, B-complex, C, calcium, magnesium, manganese, phosphorous, potassium, copper, iron, zinc, bromelain, fibre.
Beneficial properties: Anti-inflammatory, diuretic, lowers blood pressure, helps prevent blood clots, speeds up tissue repair, good for the digestive system, energy boosting.
Calorific values: 33 KCal per 100g.
Quantity/number required to make 100 ml (3 ½ fl oz): quarter-half a fruit.

Note

In the canning process and commercial juicing process, some of the beneficial properties of pineapple are lost. If using canned fruit, use those canned in natural juice, not in heavy sugar-syrup.

Preparation: Remove skin and crown of leaves and cut into pieces to fit feeder tube of juicer.

Banana

The banana as we know it is a hybrid with sterile, seedless fruits that grow on a giant herb: it's probably the biggest plant that doesn't have a woody stem! A bunch of bananas is a hand, so each fruit is technically a 'finger'. With a high sugar content they are excellent energy boosters and, with the exception of raspberries, are richer in minerals than any other fruit. The starch in bananas is not easy to digest – which is why they should only be eaten when lovely and ripe (when the skin starts to show a few freckles, they're ready!) as the starch has turned to sugar. The fibre is soluble, which helps lower cholesterol, the potassium helps beat cramp and the B6 can help alleviate the worst effects of PMS.

Nutrients and active ingredients: Vitamins C, B3, B5, B6, biotin, magnesium, manganese, potassium, soluble fibre.
Beneficial properties: Stress-buster, energy-booster, stimulates the digestive system, lowers cholesterol, helps relieve cramps and symptoms of PMS.
Calorific values: 95 KCal per standard 'finger' (fruit).
Quantity/number required to make 100 ml (3 ½ fl oz): n/a. Best for smoothies.
Preparation: Remove peel.

Guava

This small tropical fruit originated in Mexico and grows on small bush-like trees. It is part of the Myrtaceae family, which includes cinnamon, cloves, allspice and nutmeg. There are over 100 species of guavas, ranging in size from small tangerines to large oranges, but the most distinctive feature is their aroma which can be exceptionally sweet – or absolutely vile! Fortunately the guavas we eat are gorgeous in both scent and taste and are rich in Vitamin C – especially the pink-fleshed varieties. Mixed with natural live yoghurt, guavas make some of the most luxurious smoothies on earth!

Nutrients and active ingredients: Vitamins A, C, B3, soluble fibre, nicotinic acid, phosphorous, calcium.
Beneficial properties: Antioxidant, immune boosting, detoxifying, anticancer, lower cholesterol, mildly laxative.
Calorific values: 25 KCal per average fruit.
Quantity/number required to make 100 ml (3 ½ fl oz): 2.
Preparation: Remove skin and seeds.

Figs

These ancient fruits appeared in the Bible – the leaves worn by Adam and Eve – and under a species of fig tree, the bo, Gautama sat and Buddhism was born. The common fig is a member of a large family of around 800 species growing throughout India, the Near East, Turkey, Greece and the Mediterranean. The Indian species of fig *Ficus religiosa* is known as the 'sacred fig' and Hindus believe the wood was used for the original sacred fire with which the gods gave humans knowledge. A second fig, the banyan, is also sacred to the Hindus and is used in Ayurvedic medicine. In ancient Greece Olympic athletes were fed figs to build up their stamina and strength, and the Romans believed the fig tree to be sacred as the wolf, which rescued Romulus (the founder of Rome) and Remus, rested underneath one. This mystical and ancient fruit is now known to be a rich source of benzaldehyde, an anticancer agent.

Nutrients and active ingredients: Vitamins A, B-complex, calcium, magnesium, phosphorous, potassium, fibre.
Beneficial properties: Anticancer, energy-boosting, boosts the digestive system, helps treat anaemia, also purported to be an aphrodisiac!
Calorific values: Fresh: 43 KCal per 100g. Dried: 213 KCal per 100g. (It takes 3 lb. of fresh figs to make 1 lb. of dried! A dried fig is about 50% sugar, hence it high calorie value).

Quantity/number required to make 100 ml (3 ½ fl oz): n/a.
Preparation: Fresh: cut open and scoop out flesh. Dried: Rehydrate by soaking in water.

Warning !

Dried figs should be moist and sweet smelling: avoid dried out, mouldy or sour smelling figs (they are fermenting!)

Dates

Archaeological evidence shows that date palm cultivation was already established in Mesopotamia by 3500 BC and they continue to form an important food crop throughout the Middle East. For the Bedu who roam the desert, figs and dates form their staple diet. Dates can be used as substitutes for sugar, as a staple food, and even for making an incredible strong alcoholic drink! Dried dates can also be ground into flour. It is the mineral content of dates – especially their iron content – which is of interest to contemporary scientists. The amount of iron in a date is dependent on the variety, not on the amount in the soil! Just 10 Gondela dates from the Sudan will provide more than the daily requirement of iron, while 14 dates of the Khidri variety from Riyadh do the same. Of the 100 or so varieties, the dates we are most likely to find are Deglet Noors (from Algeria) and Medjools (from Morocco) and the Zahidi, Barhi, Halawi and Khadrawi dates from Iran – although all these varieties are now grown outside these countries, especially in the USA.

Nutrients and active ingredients: Vitamins C (fresh only), B-complex, folate, iron (which varies between variety), potassium, fibre.
Beneficial properties: Energy booster, helps treat anaemia, used in treatments for ME, mildly laxative.
Calorific values: Fresh: 95 KCal per 100g. Dried: 248 KCal per 100 g.
Quantity/number required to make 100 ml (3 ½ fl oz): n/a.
Preparation: Fresh: remove stone.

Food Facts – Vegetables

Vegetables, like fruit, are nature's storehouses of goodness. Rich in vital vitamins and minerals, for hundreds of years their health giving properties have been known and are, more recently, the subject of scientific enquiry. Like fruits, raw vegetables can also be juiced to extract as many of the vital nutrients as possible. Some of the flavours are strong, while others are surprisingly sweet!

Wherever possible choose organically grown vegetables: commercially grown vegetables are grown using organo-phosphate pesticides of which there may be a toxic residue. Wash all vegetables thoroughly prior to juicing.

Root vegetables

Carrots

Carrots belong to a family that has about 2,500 members, including parsley, caraway, dill and celery, and there are several hundred varieties of carrots in different shapes and sizes. They are believed to have originated in Afghanistan and are derived from the wild carrot known as 'Queen Anne's Lace': cultivated and wild carrots, if crossbred, produce a carrot with a whitish root. The orange colour is the result of the betacarotene content: a single carrot has enough for your body to convert into a whole day's supply of Vitamin A – vital for healthy skin, night vision and the disease-resistant mucus membranes.

Nutrients and active ingredients: Vitamins A, C, E, K, folate, calcium, manganese, phosphorous, chromium, iron, zinc, betacarotene, fibre.

Beneficial properties: Anticancer, antioxidant, good for skin and eyes, good for the heart and circulation.

Calorific values: 25 KCal per 100g.

Quantity/number required to make 100 ml (3 ½ fl oz): 2.

Preparation: Scrub, top and tail. No need to peel.

Beetroots

So revered was this humble vegetable that the ancient Greeks offered it up as a sacrifice to the god Apollo at his temple in Delphi – although it is likely that the priests who interpreted the oracles ate them! Although beetroot has been used for hundreds of years by Romany gypsies and many people in Russia and Eastern Europe as a tasty and nutritious food and as a 'medicine', especially in cancer treatments, it is only recently that it has attracted the attention of scientists in the west. Research is now beginning to explain how the deep red colour of the beetroot contains anti-carcinogens and how the vegetable encourages the body's cells to absorb increased amounts of oxygen. Its red colour has also made it useful in treating disorders of the blood such as anaemia and leukaemia.

Nutrients and active ingredients: Folate, calcium, manganese, potassium, iron, betanin, malonic acid, phytosterol, saponin, protein, fibres.

Beneficial properties: Anticancer, anti-inflammatory, antioxidant, immune boosting; boosts cell oxygenation, rejuvenating, detoxing.

Calorific values: 36 KCal per 100g.

Quantity/number required to make 100 ml (3 ½ fl oz): ½ small beetroot.

Preparation: Scrub and remove the fibrous stalk at the base.

Warning !

Warning ! Don't panic if your stools or urine are bright red after eating beetroot! It's only the betanin, natural colour of the vegetable passing through.

Radishes

Originally native to southern Asia, radishes are now widely cultivated throughout China, Europe and Japan. The ancient Egyptians cultivated radishes and paid the workers building the pyramids in radishes, garlic and onions. Like cabbage, broccoli and brussels sprouts, radishes are part of the Cruciferae family and contain sulphurous compounds, which have valuable anti-carcinogenic properties.

Nutrients and active ingredients: Vitamin C, folic acid, selenium, potassium, calcium, sulphur, glucosilinates.
Beneficial properties: Anticancer, stimulates discharge of bile.
Calorific values: 1 KCal per radish.
Quantity/number required to make 100 ml (3 ½ fl oz): n/a - for flavour only.
Preparation: Wash thoroughly.

Florence Fennel

Although not a powerhouse of vitamins and minerals, fennel in the bulb form – the seeds have been used medicinally for thousands of years – has numerous volatile oils that impart a unique flavour.

Nutrients and active ingredients: Vitamin A, volatile oils, including anisic acid, fenchone, limonine, anethole.
Beneficial properties: Diuretic, boosts the digestive system, good for treating flatulence.
Calorific values: 50 KCal per 100g.
Quantity/number required to make 100 ml (3 ½ fl oz): 1.
Preparation: Wash thoroughly to remove sand.

Note:

A fresh fennel bulb should have crisp, green leaves at the top of the stalks. If these have been cut off, it is probably because they were old, which indicates a bulb that is past its prime.

Bulbs

Onions

Onions belong to the same family as leeks, garlic, spring onions, chives and shallots. Like garlic, the onion is currently undergoing extensive medical research, which is fast confirming its reputation as a cure-all that is especially effective on the circulatory system, helping to break down blood clots. Antibacterial, onions have been used to treat chest infections.

Nutrients and active ingredients: Vitamins B, C, calcium, magnesium, potassium, allinase.
Beneficial properties: Powerful diuretic, antibacterial.
Calorific values: 22 KCal per 100g.
Quantity/number required to make 100 ml (3 ½ fl oz): 2.
Preparation: Peel. If you peel onions under water – the onions, not you – it is said that you won't shed so many tears!

Spring Onions (Scallions)

Onions probably originated in southern Asia or India but they have been grown and eaten since recorded history. Wild onions grew in North America: the Native North Americans around the Great Lakes region called them *she-khe-ony*, which may have given the city of Chicago its name! A spring onion, with the bulb end inserted in the ear, is said to relieve ear ache!

Nutrients and active ingredients: Vitamins B, C, calcium, magnesium, potassium, allinase.
Beneficial properties: Diuretic, antibacterial.
Calorific values: 22 KCal per 100g.
Quantity/number required to make 100 ml (3 ½ fl oz): n/a. Use chopped for garnish.
Preparation: Wash and trim off the hairy roots – leave the dark green leaves on!

Leeks

So important were leeks in the staple diet of medieval Europeans that the old Anglo Saxon word 'leek' once meant any vegetable. On St. David's Day, proud Welsh wear a leek in their buttonholes to commemorate the victory in 690 AD of the Welsh king Cadwaller over the Saxons. At the battle, their forefathers wore a leek to distinguish themselves from their enemy. Perhaps the close contact with this vegetable accounts for the magnificent sound of Welsh choirs: the Greeks and Romans believed leeks were good for the throat. Emperor Nero ate them every day to improve the quality of his voice!

Nutrients and active ingredients: Vitamins A, B complex, C, calcium, magnesium, folic acid, betacarotene (in green leaves), potassium.
Beneficial properties: Antibacterial, anticancer, diuretic, eliminates uric acid, reduces high blood pressure and cholesterol levels, good for sore throats.
Calorific values: 18 KCal per 100g.
Quantity/number required to make 100 ml (3 ½ fl oz): 1 large.
Preparation: Wash and trim off hairy roots. Leave on as much of the dark green leaf as possible.

Garlic

When the Romans conquered a new territory, the first herb they planted was garlic. It arrived in Britain with Roman centurions who wedged cloves between their toes to stop fungal infections in the moist conditions they marched through. The antibacterial properties of garlic were first proven scientifically by Louis Pasteur in 1858. The sulphur compound allicin, which is released when garlic is crushed, lowers cholesterol. In addition to keeping vampires away, many people have found that taking garlic – even the odourless garlic pearls available in health food shops – for 2 weeks before going on holiday, stops mosquitoes from biting them!

Nutrients and active ingredients: Vitamin B6, magnesium, phosphorous, potassium, iron, zinc, bioflavinoids, glucokinin, mucilage, phytohormones, volatile oils.
Beneficial properties: Antibacterial, anticoagulant, anticatarrhal, antioxidant, antiseptic, expectorant, detoxer, lowers blood pressure, lowers cholesterol, keeps vampires away!
Calorific values: 3 KCal per average clove.
Quantity/number required to make 100 ml (3 ½ fl oz): n/a - for flavour only.
Preparation: Peel and crush or chop cloves.

Brassicas

The brassica family – of which cabbage, cauliflower, and brussels sprouts are the best known – is valued for Vitamin C and betacarotene and, increasingly, their anticancer properties.

Warning !

People with sensitive skins should be careful when handling all brassicas, which can cause contact dermatitis.

Warning !

All members of the brassica family should only be eaten in modest amounts by people taking thyroid medication (thyroxine) or iodine for under-active thyroids. Brassicas contain goitrogenic factors, which interfere with the thyroid's ability to absorb iodine.

Cabbage: Red, White and Savoy (Dark Green)

The 'medicine of the poor' is how the cabbage has been honoured throughout history: the Romans used them for treating tumours, and they do have anticancer properties attributed to the presence of phtyochemicals, such as glucosinolates. As soon as the vegetables are chopped, the glucosinolates are released and converted into anti-carcinogenic indoles. The dark green leafy Savoy cabbage is by far the 'super cabbage' with a high Vitamin C content, folate, and betacarotene.

Nutrients and active ingredients: Vitamins C, A (Savoy), B3, folate, calcium, potassium, iron, sulphur compounds.
Beneficial properties: Anticancer, antioxidant, energy-boosting.
Calorific values: Red: 19 KCal per 100g. White: 24 KCal per 100g. Savoy: 25 KCal per 100g.
Quantity/number required to make 100 ml (3 ½ fl oz): ⅓ small cabbage.
Preparation: Wash and chop.

Kohlrabi

Although it doesn't contain any betacarotene, the kohlrabi is rich in potassium, a good source of Vitamin C and folic acid. Its German name translates as 'cabbage turnip' and, despite its looks, it is a crucerous vegetable descended from the original wild cabbage. It arrived in Germany in the 1500s, since when it has been a very popular foodstuff. In terms of nutrients and health benefits, kohlrabi is almost identical to cabbage.

Nutrients and active ingredients: Vitamins C, A (in the green tops), B3, calcium, folate, potassium, iron, sulphur compounds.

Beneficial properties: Anticancer, antioxidant, energy-boosting.

Calorific values: 23 KCal per 100g.

Quantity/number required to make 100 ml (3 ½ fl oz): 1 small/ ½ large.

Preparation: Wash.

Spinach

Spinach originated in Persia, and spread eastwards via China and Korea to Japan. It travelled westwards with the Arabs to Spain in the 11th century and was in widespread use throughout Europe by the end of the 17th century. The large amounts of iron – as every Popeye fan knows – that are present in spinach are, in fact, not easily absorbed in the body because of the presence of oxalic acid. This combines with the minerals, which are then excreted out of the body as insoluble salts. But it is an excellent source of chlorophyll, which is beneficial to the blood and rich in folic acid: if you are considering having a baby, then boost your spinach intake!

Nutrients and active ingredients: Vitamins A, E, B2, B3, folate, calcium, iron, magnesium, manganese, potassium, zinc, carotenoids (lutein and zeaxanthin), chlorophyll, oxalic acid, fibre, protein.

Beneficial properties: Anticancer, antioxidant, anti-viral, immune-boosting, good for sight protection, energy-boosting.

Calorific values: 23 KCal per 100g.

Quantity/number required to make 100 ml (3 ½ fl oz): 20 large leaves.

Preparation: Wash and pat dry.

Warning !

Foods containing oxalic acid are best avoided if you are suffering from kidney or bladder stones, or rheumatoid arthritis.

Curly Kale

The main ingredient, along with mashed potatoes, of the hearty Dutch dish stampot is curly kale. It almost certainly started life in the eastern Mediterranean, but because it is so hardy – able to withstand temperatures down to –15 degrees C/5 degrees F, as well as high summer temperatures – it now grows throughout the world and deserves a much bigger place in our diets, not only for its taste but for its anticancer properties and huge amounts of betacarotene – as do all the dark green leafy vegetables such as collard, spring and mustard greens.

Nutrients and active ingredients: Vitamins A, C, B2, B3, B6, E, folate, calcium, phosphorous, potassium, manganese, bioflavinoids, iron, zinc, glucosinolates, protein, fibre.
Beneficial properties: Anticancer, antioxidant, stress-buster, energy-booster, detoxifier.
Calorific values: 33 KCal per 100g.
Quantity/number required to make 100 ml (3 ½ fl oz): 1 large handful of leaves.
Preparation: Wash and pat dry.

Broccoli

The name broccoli is derived from the Latin *brachium* which means 'arm' or 'branch'. With twice as much Vitamin C as an orange and as much calcium as whole milk, broccoli is indeed a 'superfood' and, like other members of the cruciferous family, broccoli has been shown to have protective powers against cancers.

Nutrients and active ingredients: Vitamins A, B-complex, C, E, iron, folate, calcium, phosphorous, potassium, glucosinolates, fibre, protein.
Beneficial properties: Anticancer, antioxidant, blood-booster, energy-booster, helps improve anaemia and fatigue, good for the heart and circulation.
Calorific values: 33 KCal per 100g.
Quantity/number required to make 100 ml (3 ½ fl oz): 6–8 florets.
Preparation: Wash, dry, and break into florets. Leave stalks on!

Salad vegetables

Celery

Hippocrates, the father of medicine, used celery to treat nervous patients and it was also highly prized by the Romans for its medicinal values. Until the late 16th and early 17th centuries in Europe, celery was grown only for this purpose, not for the table. It does calm the nerves – especially the essential oils, which are extracted from the seeds – and has been shown to reduce high blood pressure. Traditionally it has been used to treat rheumatism and gout: its diuretic properties make it a useful detoxifier and expeller of uric acid.

Nutrients and active ingredients:
Vitamins A, C, B-complex, E, calcium, magnesium, phosphorous, potassium, sodium.
Beneficial properties: Diuretic, detoxifier, stress-buster, can help relieve arthritic conditions, and is said to help break up gallstones.
Calorific values: 18 KCal per 100g.
Quantity/number required to make 100 ml (3 ½ fl oz): 2 stalks.
Preparation: Wash, leave on as much green leafy top as possible.

Note:

Go for the greenest celery you can find: while blanched celery (the pale green-white colour) is less bitter, it has fewer nutrients than unblanched. Where possible, buy organic as celery accumulates synthetic nitrates from fertilisers.

Cucumber

India is credited as the country where cucumbers originated but cucumber seeds found near the Burma-Thailand border have been carbon dated by archaeologists as far back as 7750 BC! Wherever it's hot, there are refreshing cucumbers. The expression 'cool as a cumber' is quite true: the inside of a cucumber can be up to 20 degrees lower than the outside temperature! It contains more than 95% water – more than any other food except its relative, the melon. But cucumbers also have some Vitamin A and potassium and are amazingly high in Vitamin E, which is effective as a skin treatment and why cosmetic companies are keen to include it in their beauty preparations!

Nutrients and active ingredients: Vitamins A (with skin intact), E, potassium.
Beneficial properties: Detoxifier, therapeutic for the skin and eyes, mildly diuretic, refreshing and cooling to the skin and intestines.
Calorific values: 10 KCal per 100g.
Quantity/number required to make 100 ml (3 ½ fl oz): ½ large cucumber.
Preparation: Wash, but don't peel as the skin contains the carotenoids, which the body transforms into vitamin A.

Lettuce

Descended from the wild lettuce much prized by the ancient Romans for its milky juice, which can be used to treat sunburnt skin, and has a calming, mildly sedative effect. Over 90% water and only 7 KCals per 100g, it's not surprising lettuce is the slimmer's super-food. But it is, in fact, a lot more than water: there are many minerals contained in this leafy delight. As a general rule, the darker the leaves, the more full of goodness they are, with greater amounts of betacarotene.

Nutrients and active ingredients: Vitamin C, betacarotene, folic acid, calcium, potassium, iodine, iron.
Beneficial properties: Good for insomnia, stress-buster.
Calorific values: 7 KCal per 100g.
Quantity/number required to make 100 ml (3 ½ fl oz): about half a big head.
Preparation: Wash thoroughly. Where possible, buy organic as lettuce accumulates synthetic nitrates from fertilisers.

Warning !

The milky sap from broken stems and the 'juice' made from lettuce can irritate the eyes, so take care to wash your hands after handling.

Watercress

Watercress is rich in antioxidants that help fight against cancer. Hippocrates recognised its health-giving properties and even built the world's first hospital adjoining a flowing stream, where he could grow fresh watercress for his patients. Both the Greeks and Romans believed in its power to cure madness, while Nicholas Culpepper regarded it as a preventative for scurvy. Most importantly, the benzyl mustard oil which gives watercress is 'bite' is also a powerful antibiotic, but doesn't harm the levels of flora in the gut.

Nutrients and active ingredients: Vitamins A, C, E, B3, B6, calcium, manganese, iron, glucoinolates, volatile oil, iodine, protein, fibre.
Beneficial properties: Anticancer, antioxidant, anti-scorbutic, antibiotic, purgative, expectorant.
Calorific values: 4 KCal per 100g.
Quantity/number required to make 100 ml (3 ½ fl oz): 1 large handful.
Preparation: Wash and pat dry.

Warning !

Excessive intake of watercress should be avoided by those with kidney disease.

Tomatoes

The ancestral home of the tomato is western South America – Ecuador, Peru and Chile – where wild cherry tomatoes still grow high in the mountains. The first domestication of the 'fruits' probably occurred in Mexico – the Mayan name is *xtomatl* – and they were then transported to Europe by the Spanish during the 16th century. Although thousands of varieties are known, a mere 500 varieties are available in a range of sizes, shapes and colours – including white, green, striped, orange, bell, square, vase shaped or round! The round red tomatoes are the ones we are most familiar with, and while in recent years more 'flavourful' varieties have been made available, they still never taste as good as the ones that have been grown at home – or by a neighbour – in a garden greenhouse!

Nutrients and active ingredients: Vitamins A, C, B3, E, carotenoids, potassium, low sodium.
Beneficial properties: Anticancer, antioxidant, anti-viral, immune-boosting, energy-boosting.
Calorific values: 14 KCal per 100 g.
Quantity/number required to make 100 ml (3 ½ fl oz): 3.
Preparation: Wash and remove stalks.

Peppers: Red, Green and Yellow

Sweet peppers are, with pimentos and chilli peppers, all members of the capsicum genus of the Solanaceae family, which includes tomatoes. Sweet peppers are green, and as they ripen they turn red or yellow. It was Columbus who introduced these native North American 'fruits' to Europe, where they soon spread to Africa and Asia. An important source of nutrients, Vitamins C and A and folic acid, they are also low in calories.

Nutrients and active ingredients: Vitamins A, C, B6, carotenoids, fibre.
Beneficial properties: Antioxidant, antiallergenic, anticancer, stress-busters, good for strengthening and maintaining eyesight.
Calorific values: 2–3 KCal per 100g.
Quantity/number required to make 100 ml (3 1/2 fl oz): 3.
Preparation: Rinse and chop: no need to de-seed for juicing.

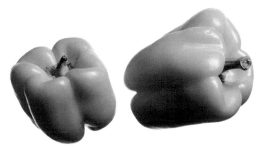

Warning !

Tomatoes are members of the Solanaceae family, which includes deadly nightshade and tobacco, and may aggravate the pain and discomfort of rheumatoid arthritis.

Warning !

Peppers are members of the Solanaceae family, which includes deadly nightshade and tobacco, and may aggravate the pain and discomfort of rheumatoid arthritis.

Food Facts – Herbs and Spices

The most ancient of western herbals, *De Materia Medica* by Dioscorides, dates from the first century AD but the use of herbs and spices is as old as humankind itself. Some of the greatest advances in medicine have their origins in the study of herbs.

Parsley

One of the most widely used herbs in cooking, all too often parsley remains on the plate as an uneaten garnish. It contains a number of essential oils and is also rich in vitamins A and C, iron, calcium and potassium. Traditionally used as an anti-inflammatory, parsley is also a powerful antioxidant, diuretic, and digestive aid. And the reason it's on your plate – it helps fragrance the breath after strong tasting and smelling foods!

Dill

Widely used in Scandinavian cookery, the lacey, feathery leafed dill takes its name from the Scandinavian word *dilla*, which means to 'lull', because of its particularly calming effects on the digestive system, relieving flatulence and stomach pains.

Rosemary

Famous for its powers of 'remembrance', rosemary is a tonic and stimulant for the brain cortex. It contains vitamin A, calcium, magnesium, iron and zinc, as well as volatile oils that make it an effective antioxidant and anti-inflammatory. It boosts circulation – which is why it is good for headaches and poor concentration. A super-food for the mind and body, rosemary is the perfect herb for when you feel 'under the weather'.

Thyme

The ancient Greeks put thyme in their baths, and the Romans used it in their house purification 'rituals' – the ancient equivalent of spring cleaning! It was also believed to give courage and be something of an aphrodisiac: medieval knights carried sprigs given to them by their ladies before jousts and tourneys. More recently, thyme was included in posies and nosegays to protect people from the smell of diseases! Its major essential oil, thymol, is an ingredient in many commercial products, but especially in antiseptics, toothpastes and mouth washes because of the soothing effects on the smooth muscles of the tracheae (wind pipe).

Basil

A relative of mint and native to India, basil stimulates the brain and the nervous system – then calms it! Like rosemary, basil also has something of a reputation for improving the memory, so it can be helpful during times of mental exertion. It is also useful in treating headaches, indigestion and flatulence. In many parts of the Mediterranean, basil eaten with the evening meal is believed to encourage a good night's sleep.

Mint

To just say 'mint' is to do a great disservice to this herb, for there are many types growing throughout the world. Peppermint and spearmint are among the most famous – although anyone with a cat will know how wonderfully relaxed (and quite silly!) they become after rolling around in a patch of catnip or catmint, or playing with a toy stuffed with the herb. Do note though that catnip is not just for cats, it's good for their owners too! Pliny the Naturalist said mint had a scent that awakened the spirit – but it also stimulates the appetite. If you've ever chewed gum and then wondered why you were hungry and your stomach was rumbling, it was the mint in the gum! Mint has an interesting property in that its smell has a warming effect on the body, which then becomes cooling and refreshing. A little mint after dinner helps the digestion and cleans the palate too!

Lemon Balm

This sweet tasting herb has a calming effect on the nerves and lowers blood pressure but it is also an antidepressant – probably because the smell and taste really 'perk' you up! If you're feeling stressed-out or fed up, try rubbing a few lemon balm leaves between your fingers and then breathing deeply of the released volatile oils. A leaf rubbed on an insect sting or bite is a good way to soothe the skin.

Sage

Its Latin name is *salvia* meaning literally 'to be saved', but more commonly, 'good health'. It's no wonder when the healing properties of this herb are considered: vitamin A, calcium, magnesium, manganese, potassium, zinc and volatile oils, which make it antiseptic and anti-inflammatory. If you have trouble with your gums, then rub them with a sage leaf! And if you have menstrual problems or are suffering from PMS, sage can help here too. (It can, however, interfere with the production of breast milk, so don't overuse this herb when breast-feeding).

Coriander

The leaves of coriander look a bit like flat-leaf parsley – which belongs to the same family – but coriander has a much more 'lemony' flavour. Rich in minerals and volatile oils, coriander has long been used by Ayurvedic physicians as a diuretic. It is also antispasmodic – it eases abdominal cramps – so it's good for digestive disturbances. An energy-booster, coriander is also said to 'enhance male potency', so girls, if you are planning to conceive, make that garnish for that special supper a bunch of coriander!

Nutmeg and Mace

These spices both come from one plant, an evergreen tree with the botanical name *Myristica fragrans*. The flavour and smell are pretty much the same, although mace is a little more bitter. Nutmeg is the more commonly used of the two, often grated over dishes. It is the myriticin that is the 'active component' in nutmeg: its effects on the brain are similar to mescaline! Consequently, it can be toxic in large doses. It stimulates the appetite, and is good if you are feeling a little queasy. In Ayurvedic medicine nutmeg is highly regarded for improving the skin.

Cinnamon

A tonic and an antiseptic, cinnamon warms the whole body and helps to beat tiredness – especially after a bout of flu. The volatile oil, which contains cinnamaldehyde, is a mild painkiller and also helps to lower raised blood pressure. And, if you feel nauseous, or have diarrhoea, a sprinkle of cinnamon can help.

Ginger

A warming and comforting remedy for travel sickness and morning sickness, as well as colds and chills, because it stimulates peripheral circulation and helps the body rid itself of toxins. Its flavour has made it one of the most widely used spices in Asian cuisine in both sweet and savoury dishes. Fresh ginger smells and tastes wonderful and can be grated or juiced. Dried ginger is also valuable, but it is much more pungent than the fresh root: a pinch to ¼ teaspoon of dried ginger is generally enough to satisfy most tastes.

Nutmeg and Mace

Ginger

Food Facts: Milk and Dairy Alternatives

Nutritionally, milk is a very valuable source of vitamins and minerals, especially for children, adolescents and during pregnancy: A, D, E, calcium, protein, zinc, B2 (riboflavin) and B12. It is also relatively inexpensive, widely available, and easily consumed. Roughly one-third of the average adult's daily protein requirement can be met with 1 pint (500 ml) of milk, along with 15% of our energy needs.

But there are drawbacks: it has a high fat content, but when the milk is skimmed or semi skimmed, the fat content is reduced – and so are the vitamins. This is why semi skimmed and skimmed milk should not be given to the under-fives.

For those with allergies – such as eczema and asthma – which can be triggered by cow's milk, there are alternatives: goat's milk and soya milk.

Soya Milk

Soya beans contain the most complete protein and lend themselves to a whole range of highly nutritious products, from tofu (bean curd) and soy sauce to soya milk, cheese and yoghurt. But it is the anticancer properties of soya that have attracted much of the attention in recent years: its antioxidant content protects against free radicals, which can lead to heart and circulatory disease as well as to cancer.

Warning !

Soya beans and soya products are a common food allergen and some people may be allergic!

Warning !

Much of the world's soya bean crop has been genetically modified: if you wish to avoid GM foods, buy organic and certified non-GM soya products!

Rice Milk

An excellent alternative to both cow's milk and soya milk is rice milk. It is also good for people who have been medically diagnosed with IBS (Irritable Bowel Syndrome) or other gastrointestinal disorders. Rice milk is now increasingly available in supermarkets – and at competitive prices too, so good health need not cost the earth!

Coconut Milk

The coconut is the largest seed known. It is believed to have been native to Malaysia, but now grows throughout the tropics, thanks to its buoyant husks being easily carried on the oceans' currents – they have been carried on the Gulf Stream across the Atlantic and been found on beaches in Scotland and even in Norway! Every 'bit' of the coconut palm can be utilised in one way or another: the fronds for roofing material; the hairy outer fibre of the nut for matting; the nut broken open for its flesh; and inside the coconut is its milky fluid, which makes a refreshing beverage. You can even use the empty shells as bird feeders or as sound effects for horse's hooves! You can buy coconut milk in cartons in shops – along with coconut cream – but in general, it has been sweetened quite highly. The tastiest and most refreshing coconut milk is that straight from the nut – because you'll have worked up a sweat cracking it!

To open a coconut, first pierce the eyes – the three 'soft spots' on the shell – and then pour out the milk. To get at the flesh, take the nut outside, put it on the pavement and hit it with a hammer. The gentler option is to place it in a 180 degrees C/350 degrees F oven for 15 minutes, then tap it all over with a hammer and remove the shell as it cracks. Don't overlook the brown skin clinging to the white flesh – this is edible and full of goodies and fibre!

Almond Milk

This is not really milk, but it's a great way to add a touch of luxury, not to say energy, to a smoothie! Almonds – as well as cashews and sunflower seeds – can be blanched or soaked and blended with water to produce a delicious, and intensely flavoured 'milk', which is high in protein (weight for weight, one-third more than eggs) – but also in calories (100g of almonds are approx. 600 KCal). They are also rich in minerals (they have the most of all nuts) like zinc, magnesium, potassium, and iron, and they also have some B vitamins.

Almonds contain oxalic acid, which combines with these minerals to carry them out of your body, so almonds are best eaten with Vitamin C rich foods – like fruit and vegetable juices! – for maximum absorption. The less water you use, the thicker the milk, but it should be strained before use. A rule of thumb is to use 1 part almond to 4 parts water. So 1 cup of nuts and 4 cups of water. You can

refrigerate the 'milk' and it will keep well for 2–3 days but it will separate, so stir it well before use.

Here's how to make it:

Ingredients

100 g (3 ½ oz) blanched almonds

1 tablespoon honey (optional)

200 ml (7 fl oz) of water and 3–4 ice cubes

Put the honey, almonds and ice cubes into a blender (make sure your machine's blades can cope with ice cubes!) and whiz them together into a smooth paste. Gradually add the water until the mixture is a smooth, milky consistency. You can drink it now or add it to smoothies in place of cow's milk, soya milk, milk rice, or yoghurt.

Warning !

If you have a nut allergy, then you will be allergic to almond milk too!

Yoghurt

One of the most ancient foods, yoghurt is a super-food: many health problems start in the guts when the balance between the good and bad bacteria is upset. The problem with commercially produced yoghurts is that although they may have been inoculated with beneficial bacteria, like *Lactobacillus acidophilus* or Bifidobacteria, because they are 'designed' to have a long shelf life. They also have a host of stabilisers, colourings, sweeteners, artificial flavourings and emulsifiers. The 'live' or 'bio' yoghurts are the ones that will help restore the balance of the bacteria in the gut. Even people who have trouble digesting milk often find they can cope quite well with yoghurt.

It's very easy to make your own yoghurt: you can buy yoghurt makers but frankly the little jars are too small, and the machines use electrical energy! The cheapest and simplest way to make yoghurt is in a vacuum flask!

Here's how:

(I use UHT milk as it only needs warming up to blood heat – not boiling and cooling down) – so it's more 'energy efficient'!)

Heat the milk gently to blood heat, add the yoghurt and dried milk and mix thoroughly with a plastic spoon (not metal). Pour into a warmed vacuum flask (or even into a bowl), which can be covered and wrapped in a towel, and left in a warm place like an airing cupboard). Seal the flask and leave overnight, or for 12 hours. The next day, voila, yoghurt! Pour out of the flask into a bowl, stir, cover and chill.

For a thicker, 'Greek Style' yoghurt, pour the yoghurt from the vacuum flask and strain off the whey – the thin liquid – from the thicker yoghurt through a piece of muslin. (You can catch the whey in a bowl and use it in the recipe on page 124 for the delicious Apricot and Apple Whey.)

When you want to make your next batch of yoghurt, simply use 2 tablespoons of your own home-made yoghurt to 'start' your next batch off.

Ingredients

1 litre UHT milk (whole)

2 tablespoons live, natural yoghurt

2 tablespoons dried milk (optional, but it makes for a thicker yoghurt)

Eye Openers and Morning Energisers

Breakfast means 'break fast' – the period of not eating when you've been asleep. If you ate supper at 7.30, went to bed at 10.30 and got up at 7.30 the next morning, your body has 'gone without' food (and water) for 12 hours! While you were sleeping, your body has been hard at work digesting and synthesising proteins, fats, carbohydrates, vitamins and minerals. There's no rest for the endocrine and digestive systems! Because our energy reserves are low – your 'sleeping' body has been busy moving nutriments to your organs – it's not surprising we are often tired when we wake up – even after a good eight hours of blissful sleep!

There is an old saying: 'Breakfast like a king, lunch like a gentleman, and dine like a pauper'. Whoever thought of this was quite right: breakfast is the most important meal of the day, the meal where we set ourselves up with energy, vitamins and minerals to last us through the day. But all too often, it is the meal that we are most likely to skip: we're late, we're rushed, or we simply can't be bothered. For some folks, the very idea of sitting down and 'eating' a balanced and nutritious breakfast is beyond belief!

It's true, it's a rare being who would consider eating a whole grapefruit or half a pineapple at one sitting – although if someone else were to prepare it beautifully and present it to us on a tray in bed (with a flower in a little vase like you see in the movies!) we'd find it hard to resist. Few of us have the luxury of a butler – or hotel room service – but that doesn't mean we should deny our bodies the vital nutrition it needs in the morning. The simplest, and the most effective way to do this is with juice. Juicing fruits – and vegetables – enables you to absorb more of the goodness of fresh produce: 4 fl oz – a good sized glassful – of pineapple or grapefruit juice is the product of juicing half of one average sized pineapple or one grapefruit! It is vital to remember that while juicing fruit and vegetables does not destroy many of the proteins and nutrients that cooking does, and while juices are easy to digest, because they lack fibre, juices should not replace entirely your intake of fruit and vegetables. Fibre is essential to the body, especially in maintaining healthy bowels.

The human body comprises 70% water and it must be replenished. We lose on average 1.5 litres (2 ½ pints) through breathing, sweating and waste excretion and it needs to be put back! To maintain optimum levels, adults should be drinking at least 1 litre (1 ½ pints) of water each day – in addition to other drinks! If caffeine is your morning waker-upper, it's worth noting that in processing tea and coffee, as (well as chocolate and carbonated drinks like colas) our bodies will actually be using water. And as caffeine is also diuretic, tea and coffee will not be replenishing the body's water supplies. Fresh fruit and veggies on the other hand, are packed with water, but their juices are much tastier than plain old water and, importantly, they are loaded with vital ingredients for your health.

Breakfast is also the time to give your brain some nutriments as well! You can improve your brain efficiency by increasing the amount of water and fruit juices you drink! In order to 'wake up' our brains and get them 'working' they need oxygen and a constant supply of glucose energy. These are delivered to the brain by the blood circulating in the body, so, for optimum 'brain storming', our diet must contain a mix of foods that provide instant energy, those that have a 'slower release' and some, like proteins, that take a longer time to break down. Most of all we need iron rich foods. However, some forms of iron are difficult for the body to absorb. We can increase the absorption by eating – or drinking – foods rich in vitamin C, especially those sunshine-filled citrus fruits.

A poor diet will not only have an impact on your physical well being, but will affect your behaviour, your ability to concentrate, your memory, your co-ordination, and your mood at the start, middle and end of each day. Vitamin B complex, folic acid, vitamins A and E are the 'super nutrients' for the brain, but there are also trace elements and 'magic minerals' such as zinc (a key factor in both memory and concentration, and found in raspberries, cantaloupe melons, avocados and yoghurt) iron (available in blackcurrants, passion fruits and prune juice), magnesium (in yummy apricots, bananas, pineapples and grapes), chromium (courtesy of apples) and selenium (yours to enjoy in tomatoes) without which our brains will not function as they should.

Apricots, apples, grapes, melons and blackcurrants are a rather delicious way of feeding your brain without becoming a food freak! Starchy fruits like bananas, which are slow to release their energy – and contain vitamin B6 to help balance the metabolism and seratonin, the body's natural 'happy chemical' – will provide you with lasting energy.

Warning

If you are ill, have or suspect you may have an allergy or food intolerance, you need to consult a doctor. The recipes suggested are NOT substitutes for medical advice or prescribed medicines!

Just Juice

It's simple, nutritious and stimulating to the brain and body. Most of the time, we only 'enjoy' freshly squeezed fruit juices when we're on holiday! Well, start every day as though it was a holiday and see how good you start to feel – especially if you start to wean yourself off that morning cup of coffee or tea!

Ingredients

1 serving

2 oranges, or 1 grapefruit, or ¼ pineapple, or 2 apples

Method

Peel your selected fruit – or wash the apples – and juice them! Pour into a glass and wake up your mind and body. Now you've got the hang of it, you can be creatively inventive with your flavours!

Wake-up Call

If absolutely nothing but coffee will get you 'up and at it' in the morning, then try this delicious, spicy iced coffee. It's especially good in summer, but is also a nice way to enjoy a midday or post lunch coffee!

Ingredients

2 servings

1 tbsp freshly ground coffee

1 tsp ground nutmeg

1 tsp ground cardamon

500 ml (1 pint) boiling water

2 tbsp vanilla ice cream

1 tbsp honey

Ice cubes

Sprinkle of cardamon to garnish

Method

Put the coffee, nutmeg and cardamon into a heatproof pot and pour on the boiling water. Leave to stand until cold. Strain into blender/food processor and blend with ice cream and honey. Pour into glasses with ice cubes and sprinkle with a little ground cardamon.

Alarm Call

This simple and delicious recipe uses cantaloupe melon, which contains carotinoids to keep the body's cells healthy.

Ingredients

2 servings

1 orange

½ cantaloupe melon

100 ml (3 ½ fl oz) white grape juice

1 tbsp ground almonds

Method

Peel and juice the orange. Slice the melon in half, scoop out the seeds and discard. Scoop out the flesh, keeping two nice bite sized pieces for garnish. Puree the remaining melon flesh in a blender/food processor and pour in the orange juice, grape juice and ground almonds. Blend briefly, pour into glasses and garnish with a piece of melon.

Orange and Raspberry Zinger

Packed full of vitamin C – and a gorgeous colour guaranteed to wake you up on even the darkest, dullest Monday mornings!

Ingredients

1 serving

2 oranges

150 g (5 oz) raspberries

Method

Peel and juice the oranges. Rinse the berries and then juice them – saving three or four for garnish. Combine the orange juice and raspberry juice in a glass and garnish with raspberries on a cocktail stick.

Good Mood

This is not only great in the morning, it's also very nice last thing at night. It's so good you could serve it at lunch or dinner parties, or at a drinks party for the non-drinkers and designated drivers! You'll need to prepare the 'grape cubes' the night before – or at least 4 hours in advance – but it's well worth this bit of extra effort!

Ingredients

2 servings

100 ml (3 ½ fl oz) white grape juice

3 oranges

100 ml (3 ½ fl oz) pear juice

Method

Pour enough grape juice to make 4–6 cubes into an ice cube tray and freeze overnight – or for at least 4 hours. Cut the oranges in half, then cut 2 slices for garnish. Squeeze the oranges and blend the juice with the pear juice and remaining grape juice. Put 2–3 'grape cubes' in each glass, pour over the juice mix and garnish with the slices of orange.

Mild Melon

This is a real 'corpse reviver' and is especially good if you feel a little light-headed or queasy first thing in the morning. On a hot day, mix it with a little cold sparkling water and serve over an ice cube for a lovely long refreshing drink.

Ingredients

1 serving

½ cantaloupe melon

2 oranges

Method

Cut the oranges in half and cut a slice for garnish. Juice the oranges. Remove the melon seeds and discard. Scoop the flesh from the melon and chop into chunks, saving a piece for garnish. Puree the melon chunks in a blender/food processor. Pour in the orange juice and whizz briefly. Pour into a glass and garnish with the chunk of melon and slice of orange.

Watermelon Wake-up

What better way to start the day with this palate cleanser packed full of goodness and vitamin C – the colour alone is a real eye-opener! You can use a juicer or a blender/food processor to make this delicious drink.

Ingredients

1 serving

⅛ watermelon

150 g (5 oz) strawberries

Ice cubes

Juicer Method

Scrub the water melon skin and juice the melon complete with the skin and pips. Remove the stalks from the berries, keep one aside for garnish, and juice the remainder. Combine the juices in a glass with 1 or 2 ice cubes and garnish with the reserved strawberry.

Blender/Food Processor Method

Scoop out the flesh and pips from the melon, cut into chunks, place in blender/food processor and whizz with strawberries.

Plum Punch

This is a delicious 'nectar' packed full of goodness. You don't have to peel the fruits if you have a juicer, but you might want to peel them if you are using a blender/food processor, or if you are sensitive to the 'fuzzy' skin. Try adding some natural live yoghurt for a really satisfying breakfast!

Ingredients

2 servings

1 peach

2 plums

1 kiwi fruit

Ice cubes

Method

Wash the fruits and pat them dry. Remove the stones – but not the skin – from the peach and the plums and peel the kiwi. Cut the fruit into chunks, reserving a slice or two of plum for garnish. Juice or whizz the fruit in a blender/food processor until smooth. Pour over ice cubes and garnish with the plum slices.

After Eight

This can be 8 am or 8 pm! Over ice, it's lovely on a balmy summer evening.
You can juice all the ingredients, or whizz them in a blender/food processor.
You can even use a good dash of 'ready made' organic, pressed apple juice
instead of the 'juiced' apple.

Ingredients

1 serving

3 kiwi fruits

1 apple

8 springs of mint –
1 set aside for garnish

Juicer Method

*Wash the fruits – peel the kiwis if you are sensitive
to the skins – and chop into chunks. Juice and pour
into glass and decorate with a sprig of mint.*

Blender/Food Processor Method

*Wash the apple, peel the kiwi, cut them into chunks
and puree in the blender with the chopped mint.*

Full Tank

This really is 'breakfast in a glass'. You can use fresh pineapple, or substitute with canned fruit in its own juice. If you don't have a juicer to tackle the apple, you can whizz it in a blender/food processor, or even use a dash of 'ready made' juice – organic or course!

Ingredients

I serving –

about 300 ml/½ pint

¼ pineapple, or about 100 g (3 ½ oz) of canned pineapple in its own juice

1 small apple, or a good dash of 'ready made' pressed organic apple juice

100 ml (3 ½ fl oz) soya milk

1 handful of alfalfa sprouts

Ice cube

Method

Remove the skin from the pineapple. Juice the pineapple, apple and alfalfa sprouts – reserving a few for garnish. Place the juices in a blender/food processor with the soya milk and an ice cube and whizz together. Serve in a tall glass and sprinkle a few alfalfa sprouts on top to garnish.

Refuel

'Break fast' and fuel up for the morning ahead with this fruity medley.

Ingredients

1 serving

*1 slice of watermelon –
about 1 in (2.5 cm) thick*

2 oranges

*¼ pineapple (or 100 g/3 ½oz
canned pineapple in its
own juice)*

Method

*Peel the oranges and the pineapple if using fresh. You can
either squeeze or juice the oranges, juice the pineapple
and the watermelon – pips and all! Combine the juices in
a glass – over ice if you like and with a fruity garnish.
Alternatively, peel all the fruit, chop it into chunks, place it
in a blender/food processor and whizz until smooth! Pour
into a glass and feel yourself recharging!*

Mellow Yellow

Now you've got the taste for juices, why not invest in a juicer and have your own freshly made supply of fruit and vegetable juices with no added sugars, salts, preservatives or artificial colours. Good food, just as nature intended it.

Ingredients

1 serving

1 apple

2 celery sticks

1 handful of alfalfa sprouts

Method

Keep a few alfalfa sprouts aside for garnish. Wash the apple and celery and juice all the ingredients. Serve in a tall glass and sprinkle on a few alfalfa sprouts.

Tropical Dawn

An excellent breakfast juice, this is also a good 'morning after' drink if you went a bit overboard the night before: the bromelain in the pineapple settles stomachs; the oranges replace lost vitamin C, and the melon will rehydrate your body.

Ingredients

1 serving

2 oranges

¼ yellow melon (Galia or Honeydew)

¼ pineapple (or 100 g /3 ½ oz canned in own juice)

1 kiwi fruit

Method

Peel and juice the oranges, pineapple (if using fresh) and the kiwi (if you are sensitive to the skins). Remove the peel and seeds from the melon and juice. Combine the juices in a glass and garnish with a slice of orange, kiwi or pineapple – or all three!

Clear Ahead

This is a real eye-opener and will also wake up your taste buds. The 'sharpness' of the radishes, which are rich in vitamin C, is smoothed away by the gentle sweetness of the carrot and apple juices.

Ingredients

1 serving

1 large carrot, scrubbed, but not peeled

1 oz (about 3–4) radishes, washed

1 large apple, washed and cored

2 ice cubes

Method

Juice the apple, carrots and radishes. Pour the juices into a blender/food processor and add the ice cubes. Whizz until blended and serve in a glass. Garnish with a slice of apple if you like.

Eye Opener

The anis flavour of fennel is a real palate cleanser – and will help deal with 'doggy breath' after a hard night's partying!

Ingredients

1 serving

1 large carrot, scrubbed
but not peeled

½ fennel bulb

Method

Juice the carrot and the fennel and serve in a glass.
Garnish with a little fennel if you like.

Power Punch

This is a terrific way to get your circulation going after lying down all night a-snooze! Blackcurrants and spinach are potassium rich, which helps to control blood pressure.

Ingredients

1 serving

150 g (5 oz) blackcurrants
6 spinach leaves
2 oranges

Method

Rinse and de-stalk the blackcurrants, keeping a few aside for garnish. Peel the oranges. Juice the blackcurrants, oranges and spinach and combine in a tall glass. Garnish with the blackcurrants or a slice of orange.

Berry Breakfast

This lovely drink can be made into a thicker, creamier and more substantial but no less healthy breakfast by adding some natural, live yoghurt. If you want to make your own yoghurt, check out the easy recipe on page 49.

Ingredients

1 serving –
about 300 ml/ ½ pint

2 small bananas – or 1 big one!

125 g (4 oz) raspberries

125 g (4 oz) blueberries – or blackberries if you prefer

125 g (4 oz) cranberries (or 1 small glass cranberry juice)

2 tbsp natural, live yoghurt

Method

Peel the bananas and clean the berries. Put the fruit into a blender/food processor and whizz until smooth. You can add the yoghurt and whizz briefly or pour the juices into a glass and swirl the yogurt on top. Either way, it's delicious!

Coriander Pear

This is a real circulation booster and the mild taste of pear and carrot juices is spiced up a little with the citrus flavour of the coriander, which is rich in vitamins and minerals.

Ingredients

1 serving

2 pears

2 carrots, scrubbed but not peeled

Small handful of fresh coriander – keep a little aside for garnish

Method

Juice the carrots and the pears with the coriander. Combine the juices in a glass and garnish with a sprig of coriander.

Get up and Go!

A wonderful sweet-sour mix of orange and prune. This combination is excellent if you are 'run down' or anaemic. The live natural yoghurt (see the recipe on page 49 to make your own) and the pinch of cinnamon will restore the balance of friendly bacteria in your gut.

Ingredients

1 serving

6 prunes (de-stoned)

2 oranges, juiced or 100 ml (3 ½ fl oz) freshly squeezed orange juice)

2 tbsp natural, live yoghurt

Pinch ground cinnamon

Method

Blend the prunes, orange juice and yoghurt together in a blender/food processor. Pour into a glass and sprinkle with a pinch of cinnamon.

Apricot and Grapefruit Tonic

If you've always avoided grapefruit in the mornings, here's a chance to enjoy this sunshine fruit in all its glory. Full of folic acid and with its high vitamin C content, grapefruit helps the body to digest the iron in the apricots. If the mix is still a little too sharp for you, add a little honey: traditional Chinese medicine uses this to improve digestion and ward off anaemia.

Ingredients

1 serving

4–6 fresh or dried apricots

1 grapefruit (or 300 ml/½ pint) grapefruit juice

1 teaspoon honey (optional)

Sprinkling ground nutmeg

Method

If using fresh apricots, remove the stones and juice them. Peel the grapefruit and juice. Combine the juices and sweeten with honey if desired. Sprinkle on the nutmeg. If using dried apricots, put the fruits into a pan and add just enough water to cover them. Cook them on a low heat until soft and 'plump', having 'rehydrated' them. Drain off the liquid, and cool the fruits.

Cramp Beater

The ginger and the sodium present in kiwis can help improve your circulation while the apples help to harmonise your digestive system.

Ingredients

1 serving

2 kiwi fruits

2 apples (or 100 ml/3 ½ fl oz apple juice)

2 cm (¾ in) fresh ginger, peeled and grated (or chopped roughly if juicing)

Juicer Method

Juice the ginger. Peel the kiwis, wash and chop the apples and juice the fruit. Combine the juices in a glass and serve with a slice of kiwi if you like.

Blender Method

Peel and grate the ginger. Peel the kiwis. Place the kiwis and ginger in the blender and pour in the apple juice. Whizz until blended and garnish with a slice of kiwi.

Winter Wake-Up

Boost your energy, eliminate toxins and fight against infections during the long winter months with this juice rich in antioxidant vitamins and minerals.

Ingredients

1 serving

3 ripe tomatoes, chopped

2 teaspoons lemon juice

3 teaspoons Worcestershire sauce

1 teaspoon soy sauce

Salt to taste

Pinch of cayenne pepper

Fresh or dried thyme to garnish

Method

Place all the ingredients – except the thyme – into a blender/food processor and whizz until smooth. Strain, serve over ice cubes and garnish with the sprig of thyme.

Morning Glory

If you're grumpy in the morning, have red eyes and a dry throat, then you need papaya (pawpaw), one of the finest cooling, anti–inflammatory foods on the planet!

Ingredients

1 serving

¼ papaya (pawpaw) – peeled and de-seeded (although bitter, they are edible and packed with goodness)

2 oranges

125 g (4 oz) cucumber (about a quarter of a cucumber is about right!)

Method

Save a slice of orange and cucumber for garnish. Wash and juice the cucumber – there's no need to peel it! Juice the oranges and the flesh of the papaya (pawpaw). Combine the juices and garnish with a slice of orange and cucumber

Green for Go!

You'll feel quite noble drinking this – it's not everyone's idea of breakfast – so why not try it for brunch instead! It is jam-packed bursting with nutrients to restore your energy and strength. High in vitamin C, iron, folic acid and vitamin E it's also got a spicy bite to it!

Ingredients

3 ripe tomatoes

4 large, washed, spinach leaves

Handful of watercress, washed

1–2 dashes soy sauce

2 teaspoons lemon juice

Pinch of cayenne pepper

Dash – or more to taste – of Worcestershire sauce

1–2 ice cubes

Pinch of thyme to garnish

Method

Blend all the ingredients together in a blender/food processor. Strain and serve garnished with a sprig of thyme – or a sprinkle of dried thyme if fresh isn't available!

Up, and Over

Hangover head? Ayurvedic practitioners have long recommended limes and grapefruits for their cleansing and restorative effects. Plenty of vitamin C, energy from natural fruit sugars, and detoxing cumin to cleanse the liver will soon have you 'up and over' your hangover!

Ingredients
1 serving

1 grapefruit (squeezed or juiced)
1 teaspoon lime juice
¼ teaspoon ground cumin

Method

Juice or squeeze the grapefruit and combine in a glass with the lime juice and cumin.

What a relief!

Cabbage juice may not be to everyone's taste – especially if you are already feeling rough from the over indulgences of the night before – although the celery and coriander do disguise the taste a great deal.

Ingredients

⅓ small green (Savoy) cabbage

1 stalk celery

Sprinkling fresh chopped coriander leaves

Method

Rinse, chop and juice the cabbage and celery. Combine in a glass and garnish with a sprinkling of chopped coriander leaves.

Life Force: drinks to boost energy and immunity

Our bodies do have the most remarkable abilities to 'heal themselves' and to ward off illness – as long as we provide them with the right energy and nutriments to allow them to function properly. Diets high in processed foods, low in fibre and high in 'false calories' that give you an immediate energy boost, but don't sustain the energy level, which is then followed by what feels like an a even deeper 'low', can deplete the body of its natural reserves of vitamins and minerals and, consequently, can leave us feeling 'run down', tired, cranky, and susceptible to illness.

Too often we suffer from common ailments and conditions such as colds, running noses, lank hair, dry or spotty skin, and chronic fatigue. These may all be signs that our immune system needs revitalising boost. Instead of reaching fc the medicine cabinet and 'over the counter' cures – which do not really cur but just relieve or mask the symptoms – try treating yourself to an energising, tasty, nutritious and natural 'remedy' courtesy of the 'food pharmacy'.

The immune system is our body's firs line of defence against micro-organisms and 'foreign bodies', protecting us by seeking out and destroying abnormal cells. When your immune system overreacts to harmless substances, it produces an allergic reaction. When it is weakened. it cannot protect you fully

Our digestive system is possibly the body's major 'point of contact' with the outside world: all food and drink pass through it before being absorbed to provide energy and nutrition. By selecting the 'right' foods and combining them with other life enhancing factors – such as taking or increasing the amount of regular exercise, lowering our caffeine and alcohol intakes, avoiding recreational drug use and giving up smoking – we can help optimise immune function.

A diet – which means a 'way of life' and not some magical weight reduction scheme! – that is based on fresh and minimally processed foods rich in vitamins, minerals, essential fats and fibres, which are known to be good for our bodies – and our 'spirits' – as they work to protect the nervous system including our brains!

The medicinal value of foods for keeping sickness at bay has been known for thousands of years. Galen, Hippocrates and the great Nicholas Culpepper, whose *Complete Herbal* was published in the 17th century, all recognised the health giving and healing properties of fruits, vegetables and herbs. With the rise of rationalism and science, many of their ideas were quickly dismissed as 'folk tales', 'old wives tales' and plain superstition.

It is only recently though that scientific research has been able to identify specifically the beneficial properties of nutriments and how they 'work'.

Research carried out by institutes such as the World Cancer Research Fund, the World Health Organisation and others, including national governments, have repeatedly confirmed that a diet high in natural fibre from fruits, vegetables and unrefined grains can protect us from a whole range of serious illnesses.

Garlic, identified by Culpepper as a remedy for 'hurts and disease', is an effective antibacterial, anti-viral, antifungal and antiparasitic remedy, and has been shown to be equivalent in its potency to antibiotics such as penicillin. Garlic is now also recognised as an anticoagulant, a means of lowering blood pressure and cholesterol. It also contains germanium and antioxidant, which promote the cellular uptake of oxygen – vital in the body's fight against mutant/abnormal cells.

The humble carrot is a veritable warehouse of nutriments, antioxidant vitamins A, B and C and valuable minerals, including iron (to combat anaemia and increase haemoglobin levels), calcium (for strong bones and teeth) and potassium (for nerves, muscle contraction and aiding the metabolism of protein and carbohydrates). Simply eating – or drinking – 2 small carrots daily can lower blood cholesterol by over 10 per cent and help to prevent heart and arterial disease!

Carotenoids – the red, yellow and orange pigments that give colour to many fruits and vegetables – seem to protect the body against some cancers, heart diseases and muscular degeneration. Because carotenoids are antioxidants, they seek and destroy rogue free radicals in cells that are known to cause disease. The carotenoids in spinach have also been found to be beneficial to the eyesight: they protect against macular degeneration, the most common cause of blindness in the over 65s.

We are indeed fortunate in our modern world that we have the means to improve our health and boost our energy through what we eat and drink: the produce shelves of most local stores and supermarkets are laden with imported fruits and vegetables that cannot be grown at home, or are out of season in our home countries, and thus allow us to experience new and exciting tastes.

However, next time you do your shopping, spend a few moments roughly calculating the 'air miles' of the contents of your basket! Think a little too about the various health giving properties of the items in your basket: get to know how good beetroot is for encouraging the production of red blood cells; how dark green leaves like curly kale can improve your skin; how live natural yoghurt helps to balance the levels of 'good bacteria' in our guts, and how avocados can stop you getting depressed! If you feel well in your body, you'll feel well in your head too!

Warning

If you are ill, have or suspect you may have an allergy or food intolerance, you need to consult a doctor. The recipes suggested are NOT substitutes for medical advice or prescribed medicines!

Borscht Cocktail

Low energy levels are an open invitation to toxins. At the first sign of a runny nose, sore throat or aching limbs, help your immune system recover and fight infection. Beetroot has long been used in Eastern Europe to sustain health through long harsh winters. Its easily assimilated sugars provide instant energy.

Ingredients

1 serving

$^{1}/_{2}$ small beetroot

2 carrots

$^{1}/_{3}$ large cucumber

1 tablespoon lemon juice

1 tablespoon live natural yoghurt

Method

Wash the vegetables and juice the beetroot, carrots and cucumber. Blend them together with the lemon juice and swirl a spoonful of live, natural yoghurt on top.

Beet Booster

A velvety-textured drink that makes a real change from ordinary 'breakfast' juices. The beetroot is native to southern Europe. The ancient Greeks offered it to their sun god, Apollo at his temple in Delphi, and mortals have been enjoying its life enhancing properties ever since!

Ingredients

1 serving
2 carrots
$1/2$ cucumber
$1/3$ beetroot

Method

Wash the vegetables – no need to peel, but top and tail and cut off the fibrous stalk at the base of the beetroot. Chop into chunks and juice the beetroot, then the carrots and then the cucumber. Combine the juices in a glass and garnish with a few slices of cucumber.

Bumpy Ride

A breakfast in a glass when you've got a tough day ahead.

Ingredients

1 serving

2 small apples

$1/2$ small beetroot

2 celery sticks

Method

Wash the ingredients and trim the stalk at the base of the beetroot. Juice the beetroot, the celery sticks and then the apples. Combine the juices in a glass – over ice is good – and garnish with a slice of apple or a celery stick.

Purple Heart

A substantial way to start your day and to clear a fuzzy head: beetroot, according to the 17th century English herbalist Nicholas Culpepper, 'purged' the head and stopped noises in the ears – it also cured toothache! Melons – especially Cantaloupes – are not only delicious, but enhance the release of energy from other foods – metabolising the natural sugars in the plums and beetroot to provide you with long lasting energy.

Ingredients

1 serving

½ small beetroot

¼ yellow melon

2 small plums

Ice cubes (optional)

Method

Wash and juice the beetroot. Remove the skin and the seeds from the melon and juice the flesh. De-stone the plums and juice them too. For a thicker juice, put all the juices in a blender/food processor with 1 or 2 ice cubes and whizz.

Avocado, Tomato and Coriander

Described as 'guacamole in a glass' : a high protein, high energy and high protection factor food, avocados started life in Peru where they were first cultivated some 9,000 years ago. Rich in potassium – a lack of which can lead to depression and exhaustion – calorie for calorie (about 275 KCal per 'pear') they offer super-nutritional value.

Ingredients

1 serving

1 avocado, de-stoned

2 tomatoes

Fresh coriander sprig

Method

Peel and de-stone the avocado. Wash and chop the tomatoes and chop some coriander. Combine all the ingredients in a blender/food processor and whizz together. Garnish with a sprig of coriander. Or sprinkle with a little chopped chive or spring onion (scallion) for extra bite and Vitamin A.

Ginger Tea

The volatile oils in ginger that give it its wonderful taste are antiseptic and immune boosting, so helping to ward off infection. Combined with the vitamin C of lemons and the sweetness of honey, this fragrant hot toddy will 'set you up' on a cold day.

Ingredients

1 serving

2 cm (½ in) thinly sliced and peeled, fresh ginger

250 ml (¼ pint) water

1 teaspoon of honey (or brown sugar)

Lemon wedge to garnish

Method

Peel and slice the ginger and simmer it in hot water for 10-15 minutes – longer if you like it stronger! Add the honey or sugar, strain through a sieve or tea strainer into a heatproof glass and garnish with a lemon wedge.

Iced Lemon and Ginger Tea

A lovely cool, refreshing and invigorating drink that's great for summer with all the added benefits of immune boosting properties.

Ingredients

4 servings

10 cm (4 in) piece of fresh ginger, peeled and sliced thinly

1 litre (2 pints) water

2 tablespoons of honey

1 tablespoon brown sugar

Zest of two lemons

1 cup fresh lemon juice

Lemon slices and a sprig of mint to garnish

Method

Peel and slice the ginger. In a medium saucepan, boil the water, honey, brown sugar, ginger, lemon juice and zest. Stir until all the sugar and honey is dissolved. Remove the pan from the heat, cover with a lid and allow the tea to infuse for 30–40 minutes. Uncover and allow to cool completely. Pour into a jug and chill. Serve over ice garnished with lemon slices and a sprig of mint.

Easy Fruit Cocktail

Refresh, refuel and revive body and soul and at the same time boost immunity from viral infections with this energising cocktail of fruits.

Ingredients

1 serving
$^{1}/_{2}$ pink grapefruit
200 g (7 oz) cranberries
2 apples
Fresh mint to garnish

Method

Squeeze or juice the grapefruit. Juice the cranberries and the apples and combine the juices in a glass, over 1 or 2 ice cubes if you like, and garnish with a sprig of fresh mint.

ACEs High

A cocktail of vitamins A, C and E, with the added bonus of protein, fat and vital minerals, such as calcium, zinc, magnesium, potassium and iron, courtesy of almonds. But because they are also high in oxalic and phytic acids, which combine with these minerals to 'sweep' them from your body, the goodness in almonds is absorbed best with a high vitamin C intake.

Ingredients

1 serving

1 nectarine – or a peach

$^1/_2$ tablespoon ground almonds

$^1/_2$ pink grapefruit

1 orange

1 pear

Method

Juice – or peel and puree – the nectarine (reserving a slice or two for garnish) and pear. Squeeze or juice the grapefruit and orange. Puree the ground almonds with the juices and blend until smooth and frothy. Pour into a glass and garnish with a little reserved fruit.

Coco-tail

A great summer 'cocktail': sustaining – thanks to the coconut – when it's too hot to eat, but full of nourishment and energy to keep you going. Papaya contains Vitamins A and C, and like most other orange-coloured fruits and veggies, it's an excellent source of betacarotene, which provides protection from the harmful effects of the sun's rays.

Ingredients
1 serving

1 nectarine or peach
$^1/_2$ papaya
$^1/_2$ pink grapefruit
1 tablespoon grated coconut
75 g (2 oz) red grapes
Chilled mineral water

Method

Wash, de-stone and juice the nectarine. Peel, de-seed and juice the papaya. Juice the grapefruit and the grapes. Mix all the juices together with the grated coconut, pour into a glass and top with chilled mineral water. Garnish with a light sprinkle of grated coconut and a few grapes.

Herbal Fruit Punch

Herbal 'tea bags' are widely available in a huge variety: fennel, borage, elder flower, lemon balm, sage, camomile, mint, peppermint, and even nettle, are just a few readily found in supermarkets and health food stores. Each herb has its own properties (see pages 42–45 for more information) and have for centuries been use to ward off and treat numerous ailments. They are simple to make – just add boiling water and a bag to a cup – but they can also be used as the base for fruit – and more intoxicating – punches too.

Ingredients

1 serving

1 herbal tea bag of your choice

150 ml (5 fl oz) boiling water

$\frac{1}{2}$ papaya

$\frac{1}{4}$ yellow melon

$\frac{1}{4}$ small pineapple

Method

Boil the water, pour over the herbal tea bag and infuse for 5–7 minutes. Peel and de-seed the papaya and melon, peel the pineapple. Puree the pineapple, melon and papaya flesh in a blender/food processor. Remove the herbal tea bag from the liquid, pour into the fruit puree and blend well. Warm a heat resistant glass by rinsing in some hot water, then pour the drink into the glass and drink slowly.

Mango magic

An exotic blend of fruits packed with energy and vitamins to power you through the day and keep your immune system in tip top order.

Ingredients

1 serving

$^1/_2$ mango

$^1/_2$ pink grapefruit

$^1/_4$ pineapple

75 g (2 oz) red grapes

Method

Peel and de-stone the mango, and juice the flesh. Remove the skin from the pineapple and juice the flesh. Juice or squeeze the half grapefruit and juice the grapes. Combine all the juices in a glass – over ice if you like – and garnish with a little fruit.

Summertime

In summer we can lose many vital minerals from our body because we tend to perspire more. While we often put the 'fluid' back in the form of water, we overlook replacing our vitamins and minerals in the 'quench quest'. Fresh fruit and vegetable juice will not only satisfy your thirst but will ensure that you don't deplete your body's energy, vitamin and minerals stores.

Ingredients

1 serving

75 g (2 oz) grapes – dark red or black ones contain more flavinoids than green ones!

$^1/_4$ yellow melon

$^1/_2$ mango

$^1/_4$ pineapple

A few grapes for garnish

Ice cubes

Method

Peel and de-seed the melon and juice the flesh. Peel and de-stone the mango and juice the flesh. Remove the skin from the pineapple and then juice this flesh. Wash the grapes, pat them dry and de-stalk then juice them too. Combine all the juices well and pour over ice cubes into a tall glass and garnish with the reserved grapes – or a bite size chunk of each fruit!

Cherry Cheer

Boost your energy with this delicious combination of cherries, blackcurrants and beetroot. Don't be alarmed at the inclusion of beetroot – its juice is surprisingly sweet – and it encourages the production of red blood cells to keep your heart, nerves and muscles in peak condition. This drink also tastes good chilled!

Ingredients

1 serving

75 g (3 $^1/_2$ oz) cherries, pitted and the stalks removed

75 g (3 $^1/_2$ oz) blackcurrants

$^1/_2$ small beetroot

Method

Wash and prepare the fruits and trim off the fibrous stalk at the base of the beetroot. Juice the beetroot, the cherries and the black currants. Combine the juices in a saucepan and gently heat through. Pour into a heat proof glass. Alternatively, pour the juices over ice into a glass and garnish with a cherry or two.

Green Goddess

Avocado to boost your energy, dill to calm the stomach, chives to cleanse the system and natural, live yoghurt to boost your 'good bacteria' levels in the gut – and to lift your spirits. Because yoghurt synthesises some of the B vitamins, it helps to prevent those 'low' periods when you feel 'blue'.

Ingredients

1 serving

1 avocado

150 ml (5 fl oz) natural, live yoghurt

Fresh dill

Fresh chives

Seasoning to taste

Mineral water (optional)

Method

Chop some chives and dill leaves finely. Peel and de-stone the avocado and chop the flesh. Puree the avocado and herbs with the yoghurt in a food processor/blender until smooth. Season to taste. If a little too thick, add a splash of mineral water. Pour into a glass and sprinkle a few chopped herbs on top.

Mangoberry

Strawberries and mango make a delicious combination that's both refreshing and energising.

Ingredients

1 serving

50 g (2 oz) strawberries

½ mango

75 g (3 ½ oz) grapes

1 apple

1 lime

Chilled mineral water
– sparkling or still

Method

Wash and hull the strawberries – keeping a nice one aside for garnish. Peel and de-stone the mango and cut up half of the flesh. Peel and squeeze/juice the lime – keep a slice for garnish too! Juice the apple. Puree the strawberries and the mango in a food processor/ blender. Pour in the lime juice and apple juice and mix well. Pour into a tall glass and top with chilled mineral water if you wish. Garnish with the lime slice and the strawberry.

Mango and Lime

A smooth blend of mango and almond milk (see the recipe on page 48 to make your own), with the tang of lime to perk up your taste buds, will strengthen your cardiovascular system and stimulate your immune system as well.

Ingredients

1 serving

1 mango, peeled and stoned

100 ml (3 $\frac{1}{2}$ fl oz) almond milk

1 lime, squeezed

1 slice of lime for garnish

Method

In a food processor/blender, whizz the mango, lime juice and almond milk together. Garnish with a slice of lime.

Veggie Cocktail

Green leaves – rocket, curly kale, watercress, spinach, spring greens, and even lettuce – are all energising and immune boosting foods and the darker the leaves, the better! Don't avoid the garlic unnecessarily: while the pungent effect on the breath may keep potential admirers (and vampires!) at bay, the builders of the pyramids fed it to their workers to give them strength; ancient Greek athletes chewed it before races at the Olympic Games to improve their chances of winning, while the Romans fed it to their legions to impart bravery!

Ingredients

1 serving

1/2 beetroot

1 handful of rocket or other green leaves

1/2 red pepper, de-seeded

1 tomato

2 celery stalks – 1 reserved for garnish

2 carrots

1 wedge of cabbage

1 clove of garlic, peeled

Seasoning to taste

Method

Wash and dry the veggies, and remove the fibrous stalk from the base of the beetroot. Juice the beetroot, the rocket leaves, the red pepper, celery, carrots, cabbage, garlic clove and the tomato. Combine the juices well in a glass, add a celery stick stirrer and season to taste.

Spicy Tomato

A nice way to liven up tomato juice, top up your energy levels and perk up your appetite. If you don't want to use chilli and garlic, try a dash of Tabasco sauce, Worcestershire sauce, or even a sprinkle of cayenne pepper instead.

Ingredients

1 serving

2 ripe tomatoes

2 celery stalks

$^1/_2$ red pepper, de-seeded

$^1/_4$ red chilli, de-seeded and finely chopped (optional)

$^1/_2$ garlic glove, crushed (optional)

Black pepper to taste

Method

Juice the tomatoes, the celery, and the red pepper. Blend the juices with the crushed garlic and finely chopped red chilli if using. Season to taste. Pour into a glass.

Watercress and Pear

Watercress was traditionally used in spring as a 'cure' to stimulate the metabolism. Today it is primarily regarded as a relief for congestion of the respiratory system and stimulator of the immune and lymphatic systems. It's packed with vitamins A, C, E, B3 and B6, plus calcium, manganese, iron, protein and fibre, all ready to work their wonders on you! Pears are, like apples, endlessly versatile and mix well with strong flavoured juices.

Ingredients

1 serving

2 ripe pears

1 big handful of watercress

Ice cubes (optional)

Method

Wash the pears and remove the stalks. Wash the watercress and pat dry. Juice the watercress and the pears and combine the juices in an ice filled glass. Garnish with a stem of watercress.

Cabbage and Carrot

It's no wonder that cabbages were once known as 'the poor man's physician': they are high in fibre, low in calories, rich in Vitamins B and C, bioflavinoids, potassium, and folic acid. The ancient Greeks valued its properties so much that laws were passed making the stealing of cabbages punishable by death! Cabbage juice can politely be described as 'an acquired taste', but its taste is improved by mixing with another, sweeter juice, such as carrots, and some celery for 'spice', to make a really good energiser that will help ward off colds and flu.

Ingredients

1 serving

$^1/_3$ small cabbage – this can be red, white or best of all, dark green

2 carrots

2 celery stalks

Fresh coriander to garnish

Method

Wash the veggies and juice the cabbage, celery and carrots. Mix the juices well in a glass and garnish with a little fresh coriander.

Sunny

A great way to start – and enjoy the day – full of energy!

Ingredients

1 serving

1 apple

2 carrots

1 orange

Fresh mint sprig

Method

Wash and juice the carrots. Cut a slice – or a small wedge – from the orange for garnish and squeeze the rest. Wash and juice the apple. Mix the juices in a glass and garnish with the piece of orange and a sprig of fresh mint.

Spiced beet

A terrific mid-morning, or, mid-afternoon juice for restoring energy. The beetroot will help raise the body's iron levels and build up your strength to tackle the rest of the day.

Ingredients

1 serving

2 carrots

1 orange

$^1/_4$ beetroot

2 cm (1 inch) piece of fresh ginger

Slice of orange for garnish

Method

Wash the beetroot, trim off the fibrous stalk at the base and juice. Wash and juice the carrots. Peel and juice the ginger and peel and juice the orange. Combine the juices in a glass and garnish with a slice of orange.

Apricot and Ginger

Apricots were the nectar of the gods in ancient Greece and Rome and their vibrant gold colour marks them out as being rich in Vitamin A and betacarotene. Packed with nutriments, apricots are nourishing and strengthening and make an ideal fruit for anyone feeling tired and run down.

Ingredients

1 serving

5–6 apricots, de-stoned

2 small apples

100 ml (3 ½ fl oz) milk (soya, rice, cow's, goat's, whichever you prefer)

1 teaspoon of fresh ginger, peeled and chopped finely

Method

Wash, stone and juice the apricots. Wash and juice the apples. Place the juices in a blender/food processor with the ginger and milk and whizz together. Pour into a glass. Garnish with a little fresh apricot if you like.

Beet and Apple

A real nutrition packed energiser, full of vitamins and minerals –
and it tastes great too!

Ingredients

1 serving

3 small apples

$^1/_2$ small beetroot

Method

Wash and trim off the fibrous stalk of the
beetroot and then juice half of it. Wash
the apples, then juice them. Combine the
juices in a glass – over ice if you like –
and feel yourself coming 'back to life'!

Carrot, Lemon and Garlic

Carrot juice is one of the easiest and nicest drinks. It can be a little sweet on its own, so try it with a bit of 'zing' from lemon and garlic.

Ingredients

1 serving

2 carrots

$\frac{1}{2}$ lemon

1 clove garlic, peeled

Black pepper (optional)

Method

Wash the carrots and juice them. Juice or crush/chop the garlic very finely – the finer it is the more 'dispersed' the flavour. Juice the $\frac{1}{2}$ lemon. Combine all the juices in a glass and serve garnished with a sprinkle of black pepper.

Green Peace

This is a surprisingly mild flavoured drink. It uses those dark green leaves of curly kale – one of the tastiest members of the cabbage family – whose properties include moving oxygen to the body's tissues and helping the body to release energy contained in foods. If you're feeling 'sluggish', this drink will give your body a much needed boost.

Ingredients

1 serving

4 small broccoli florets

1 small handful of curly kale leaves

1 small celery stalk

1 apple

1 small bunch parsley, with a sprig reserved for garnish

Method

Wash and dry the vegetables and the apple. Juice the broccoli, the kale, the celery, the parsley and the apple and combine the juices in a glass. Garnish with a sprig of parsley.

Leafy Lunch

A light refreshing drink with a peppery and herby bite imparted by the dark green leaves of rocket or watercress

Ingredients

1 serving

2 apples

150 g (5 oz) white grapes

25 g (1 oz) rocket or watercress

Small 'bunchlet' fresh coriander,
a little saved for garnish

$^1/_2$ lime, squeezed or juiced, with
a slice reserved for garnish

Method

Wash and pat dry the ingredients. Juice
the apples, the watercress or rocket, the
coriander and the grapes. Squeeze or
juice half a lime. Combine all the juices
in a glass and decorate with a lime slice.

Green Park

Also known as Finocchio and Anise, Florence fennel, when raw, has a delicate flavour that's a sort of cross between celery and liquorice. In Greek, fennel is called *marathon*: In 490 BC the Greeks defeated the Persians in a battle fought in a fennel field and runners raced just over 42 kilometres (26 miles) to bring news of the victory back to Athens! Fennel is a good source of Vitamin A – and it's low in calories. While we can't guarantee an Olympic gold medal, this drink will give you plenty of energy to race through the day!

Ingredients
1 serving
1/2 Florence fennel bulb
1/3 small red cabbage
2 apples
1/2 lemon

Method
Chop the cabbage and juice it. Remove the stalk from the Florence fennel and juice. Chop the apples and juice them too. Peel the lemon, keep a slice or a wedge aside for decoration, and juice half of it. Combine the juices in a glass and garnish with the lemon slice.

Tropical Berry

This really luxurious drink – more like a meal – blends tropical fruits with blackcurrants and strawberries. It's a real 'pick-me-up', full of vitamin C and immune boosting properties. You can make this in a juicer or blender/food processor and serve over ice cubes or crushed ice, or even add some natural live yoghurt for a rich smoothie.

Ingredients

1 serving

1 guava, peeled

$^1/_2$ papaya, de-seeded and peeled

1 small banana

50 g (1 $^3/_4$ oz) blackcurrants

50 g (1 $^3/_4$ oz) strawberries – with one reserved for garnish

Method

Wash and prepare the fruits. Place in a blender/ food processor and whizz them together until smooth. Pour into an ice filled glass and garnish with the strawberry.

Guavapple

Guavas are really rich in vitamin C: one average fruit supplies about five days requirements! Even canned guavas, though they lose some in the processing, still manage to hang onto two-thirds of their original Vitamin C content!

Ingredients

1 serving

1 guava, peeled

2 apples

Slice of lime, lemon or orange to garnish

Method

Peel and scoop out the flesh from the guava. Juice the apples, combine with the guava flesh and mix well. Pour into a glass and garnish with a slice or two of lemon, lime or orange.

Ginger Leeks

Leeks have been used as food and medicine for some 4,000 years: the ancient Greeks and Romans valued them highly for throat problems and the infamous Roman emperor, Nero, ate them every day to improve his singing voice! As a member of the allium family – garlic, chives and onions – leeks are a good source of potassium, folic acid and, in the dark green leaves at the top, of betacarotene, which the body converts to vitamin A. The 'oniony' taste of leeks is here tempered by sweet apples and ginger.

Ingredients

1 serving

1 small leek – with as much green on top as possible

3 apples

2 cm (³/4 in) piece of peeled ginger

Method

Slice the 'hairy roots' off the leek, but leave on the green tops. Peel the ginger. Wash and chop the apples. Juice the leeks, the ginger and then the apples. Combine the juices in a glass. Garnish with a slice of apple if you like.

Apple Leek

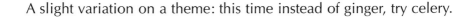

A slight variation on a theme: this time instead of ginger, try celery.

Ingredients

1 serving

1 small leek

2 apples

2 stalks celery –
1 reserved for garnish

Method

Trim the roots off the leek, but leave on the green tops. Wash and chop the apples. Wash the celery – leave on those lovely leafy bits at the top too! Juice the leeks, then one of the celery sticks and then the apples. Combine the juices in a glass and garnish with the remaining celery stick.

Creak Juice

If you're feeling a bit tired and starting to ache around the shoulders and back, try this combination whose properties are reputed to ease pain. If you eat your garnish, you won't have to worry about your breath: parsley is renowned as 'nature's breath freshener'.

Ingredients

1 serving

2 small leeks

2 carrots

Sprig of parsley with
a little reserved for garnish

Method

Trim the roots from the leeks and wash the carrots. Juice the leeks, the carrots and the parsley. Combine the juices in a glass and decorate with a sprig or two of parsley.

Cool Cue

Because of their high water content, cucumbers are very refreshing and low in calories – which compensates for the fact that their mineral and vitamin content is quite low. They are great for perking you up when you feel like you are 'wilting' in a hot, dry office environment. You can even cut a few slices and pop them over tired eyes if you've been staring too long at a computer screen!

Ingredients

1 serving

$^1/_2$ cucumber

1 tomato

$^1/_2$ green pepper, de-seeded

1 clove garlic, peeled (optional)

2 sprigs of fresh dill, one reserved for garnish

Method

Wash and prepare the ingredients and juice the tomato, green pepper, garlic (optional) cucumber and one sprig of dill. Combine the juices in a glass and garnish with the reserved sprig of dill and a slice of cucumber or two.

Grapefruit and Black

Yellow grapefruits are often less expensive than pink or 'ruby' ones. Most people's first encounter with this juicy fruit is with the yellow variety, whose sharp taste can be a bit off-putting. Blended with a second fruit, however, these yellow 'globes of sunshine' become sweet and palatable!

Ingredients

1 serving

1 grapefruit

1 apple

75 g (3 oz) or so of blackcurrants

Method

Peel the grapefruit – keep a slice for garnish. Rinse the blackcurrants and remove the stalks. Wash and chop the apple. Juice the blackcurrants, followed by the grapefruit and then the apples. Combine the juices in a glass and garnish with a little fresh fruit.

Carrot, Orange and Coriander

If your throat and nose are congested, try this aromatic medley. This is a really 'cleansing' mix – a nice way to end the work day and prepare for play!

Ingredients

1 serving

2 carrots

1 orange

Small bunch of coriander, with a sprig or two reserved for garnish

Ice cubes

Method

Wash and juice the carrots and apple. Chop the coriander finely. Put a few ice cubes in a glass, pour in the juices and stir. Garnish with a sprig or two of fresh coriander.

Garlic Gargle

This is a great drink for harnessing the antioxidant and anti-viral properties of garlic. An actress friend recommends this drink if you know you are going to be outside in the wind and rain. You can prepare your body in advance to help it fight off cold germs. The betacarotene in the carrots helps tone the mucous membranes and eases breathing too! If you eat the sprigs of parsley afterwards, it'll take care of garlicky breath!

Ingredients

1 serving

2 cloves garlic

4 carrots

3 – or more – sprigs of parsley

Method

Wash the carrots and juice them. Peel the garlic cloves and juice them too. Mix the juices well in a glass and garnish with a liberal helping of parsley.

Berry Blast

This is so nice, you can serve it at dinner parties instead of wine!

Ingredients

1 serving

1 lemon

2 oranges

125 g (4 oz) raspberries

Sprig of lemon balm
or fresh mint

Method

Peel the oranges and the lemon. Rinse the raspberries and juice them. Juice the oranges and the lemon. Combine the juices in a glass and garnish with a little of the fruits and a sprig of lemon balm or fresh mint.

Mango Smoothie

A really reviving drink with a slight tang of lime. If you can't find –
or don't want to use – rice milk, try it with natural, live yoghurt instead.

Ingredients

1 serving

1 ripe mango

Squeeze of lime juice

250 ml or so ($\frac{1}{2}$ pint
or so) rice milk

Fresh mint or lemon
balm to garnish

Method

*Peel and remove the flesh from the mango. Put the flesh into
a food processor/blender and add a squeeze of lime juice.
Pour in the rice milk and whizz together until smooth. Pour
into a glass and garnish with the sprig of lemon balm or mint.*

Mandarin and Lychee Smoothie

The bright red, rough skin of the lychee hides a sweet-acid flesh like a grape beneath it. They are a good source of Vitamins B and C and are great for digestion – which is why they're often served after a Chinese meal. Combined with mandarin – or clementine or satsuma – or even one of the hybrids like tangors (a mandarin-orange cross)or tangelos (a hybrid of mandarin, grapefruit and pommelo), this drink will give your potassium levels a boost and supply a good amount of folate, vital to stop you becoming tired or worse, anaemic.

Ingredients

1 serving

100 g (4 oz) lychees, peeled (canned are OK too, but drain and wash them if in syrup)

3 mandarins – or satsumas/clementines

100 ml (3 ½ fl oz) natural, live yoghurt)

Pinch of grated or ground ginger

Method

Peel the lychees and mandarins. Put them into a blender/food processor with the yoghurt and blend until smooth and creamy. Pour into a glass and dust with a sprinkle of ground or fresh grated ginger.

Cucumber Raita

Cucumber and yoghurt combine to create the cooling properties that balance the hotness of Indian curries. Even without the curry, this drink is a refreshing reviver, with the added benefits of being low in calories but beneficial to the immune system.

Ingredients

1 serving

$^1/_4$ cucumber, peeled and diced, and a couple of slices for garnish

100 ml (3 $^1/_2$ fl oz) natural live yoghurt

100 ml (3 $^1/_2$ fl oz) milk

10–12 mint leaves and a sprig reserved for garnish

Squeeze of lime juice

Pinch of salt to taste

Ice cubes

Method

Put the diced cucumber into a blender/food processor with the yoghurt, milk and mint. Whizz until blended and pour into a glass half filled with ice. Garnish with the sprig of mint and a few slices of cucumber.

Apricot and Apple Whey

The whey that Little Miss Muffet was eating alongside her curds, is the liquid – and the 'soft cheese' – left over when making hard cheeses like cheddar. Curd cheese we are familiar with – it often ends up in delicious cheesecakes. Whey can also be found floating on the top of yoghurt – and is what is strained off when you make your own (see page 49 for recipe). Regrettably, most people pour the whey away – along with its valuable lactic acid and proteins! If you really don't want to eat it, substitute with buttermilk or natural live yoghurt – and rinse your hair in the whey for extra shine instead!

Ingredients

1 serving

4 fresh apricots (or 3–4 dried apricots rehydrated by cooking in a little water till plump, then cooled and drained)

1 apple

100 ml (3 $\frac{1}{2}$ fl oz) whey or buttermilk or natural live yoghurt

Method

Wash and stone the apricots. Wash the apple. Juice the apricots and the apple. Combine the juices with the whey or yoghurt, blending well. Pour into a glass and garnish with a little apricot if you like.

Joint Juice

Rich in vitamins A and C, the combination of celery and carrots dates back to ancient Egypt. If the pyramids could be built drinking it, imagine what you alone can achieve! It's also reputed to be good for relieving aching joints, so try it after your next workout at the gym or the squash court.

Ingredients

1 serving
2 celery stalks
4 carrots
2–3 sprigs of parsley
Seasoning to taste

Method

Wash the carrots and celery and juice them and some of the parsley – keep a sprig for garnish. Combine the juices and pour into a glass. Garnish with a sprig of parsley and add a celery stick as a stirrer and for something to exercise the face muscles on!

Heart warmer

Another good, nutritious and reviving drink – perfect for after winter sports to lift the spirits and heal the body!

Ingredients

1 serving

2 carrots

$^1/_2$ small beetroot

2 celery stalks

$^1/_2$ lemon

1–2 cloves garlic (depending on whether you've got a date later on!)

2 cm (1 in) piece of fresh ginger, peeled

Method

Wash and prepare the vegetables. Juice the beetroot, the celery and the carrots. Juice the garlic, or chop very finely. Juice the ginger, or chop/grate finely. Peel and juice (or squeeze) $^1/_2$ the lemon. Combine all the ingredients, blend well together and pour into a glass. Garnish with a slice of lemon and add an extra celery stick as a stirrer.

High energy drinks

Tired? Poor concentration? Grumpy? Sounds very familiar doesn't it! In fact it's so familiar, we actually think that this is 'normal'! Too often we reach for the coffee cup, the tea pot, the canned sugar-filled drink or a bar of chocolate as a way of boosting our energy. In the short term, all these do give us a 'lift', but then they can be followed very quickly by a 'low', which leaves us feeling low – sometimes lower than we started out! Drinking three, small 'energy drinks' through the day will renew your energy and increase your activity, helping to prevent those mid-morning and mid-afternoon lows. You can even take some juice to work with you in a vacuum flask: as long as the juice is chilled first and kept cold in the flask, it will taste just as good at lunchtime as when you first made it. At home, adding a banana, which is packed with energy boosting goodness, will add bulk to your fruity treat.

Fruit juices are packed with the sugar fructose, which is an excellent energiser, so fruit juice is an excellent way to kick-start the day. But as the day wears on, most of us rely on a slower release of energy and diminishing supply! By juicing vegetables and combining them with fruit juices, a better balance is created between the energy giving fructose, the fibre, the vitamins and the minerals than would be obtained by fruit juice alone. Leafy green vegetables, because their iron content is significant, are great for restoring energy to tired bodies.

If you play sport in your spare time – or if you are trying to get a bit fitter – you need to feed your muscles. If you don't they will complain! Aches and cramps are the sign that your muscles need more minerals to be able to continue working at their maximum efficiency. Our bodies also lose minerals – in particular magnesium and potassium – as we sweat. The best way to replenish lost minerals is through fresh fruit and vegetable 'cocktails'.

Fruit and vegetable drinks also rehydrate the body, replacing the lost fluids, but it is worth noting that most 'pure juices' (except those made with really 'watery' fruits and veggies like cucumbers and melons) are really too concentrated and don't contain enough water to replace liquid lost as sweat. Sportsmen and women should dilute 'pure' juices with water – preferably mineral water with a high magnesium content. So check those labels on those water bottles!

At the end of a long day, when you arrive home, tired, and merely grunting responses to the 'how was your day' questions, you may not think an energising fruit and vegetable drink, full of vitamins and minerals, is what you need! It could be that it is the very thing you need! So don't reach for a beer or a slug of booze, reach for the juicer! The evening is to be enjoyed in the company of friends, family and lovers. Say hello to high energy: Let the day go, boost your energy levels for the evening – and night! – go ahead, and have some fun. After all, you're not at work now!

Warning !

If you are ill, have or suspect you may have an allergy or food intolerance, you need to consult a doctor. The recipes suggested are NOT substitutes for medical advice or prescribed medicines!

Banana and Date Energiser

'Candy that grows on trees' is how dates have been described. Fresh or dried, they are excellent energy snacks: they are 75–80% all-natural sugars, high in carbohydrate and food energy. They also contain potassium, calcium and magnesium as well as small amounts of vitamins A, B complex and C. Bananas are high in carbohydrates but low in fat and protein, and surprisingly, they have twice as much Vitamin C as an apple! Together they are delicious, nutritious and satisfying and this drink will provide you with long-lasting energy.

Ingredients

1 serving

300 ml (¹/₂ pint or so) milk – cow's, goat's, soya, almond, or rice milk – you choose!

2 small ripe bananas

6 dried dates with stones removed

Pinch of ground cinnamon to garnish

Method

Peel the bananas, and de-stone the dates. Cut the fruit into chunks and place in a blender/food processor with the milk and whizz until smooth. Dust with a sprinkle of ground cinnamon. (An even thicker 'drink', which is ideal for breakfast, can be made by substituting natural, live yoghurt for the milk.)

Spring fever

Four varieties of fruit to provide you with vitamins and minerals
and a kick-start to the day's activities

Ingredients

1 serving

1/2 papaya

2 kiwis

1 orange

1/2 grapefruit

*Lightly chilled
mineral water*

Method

*Peel and de-seed the papaya. Peel the kiwis, keeping
a slice or two for garnish. Puree the papaya and kiwi
until smooth. Juice (or squeeze) the orange and half
the grapefruit. Add to the puree and blend together. If
a little too thick, dilute to taste with a little lightly
chilled mineral water. Pour into a tall glass and
garnish with the kiwi slices.*

The White Stuff

If you can't find buttermilk, remember you can always substitute natural, live yoghurt. This energiser has the added bonus of a little (note 'little'!) grated chocolate on top – and why not? Sometimes, nothing else except chocolate will do to give you a real boost. It was called the 'food of the gods' by the Aztecs, but it is available for mere mortals to enjoy too! And chocolate is rich in phenylethylamine – the same substance manufactured by the brain when you are in love!

Ingredients

1 serving

1 kiwi fruit

1 small banana

1 small apple

75 ml (2 fl oz) buttermilk, or natural live yoghurt

Lightly chilled mineral water

A little grated chocolate

Method

Wash the apple and juice it. Peel the kiwi and banana, reserving a slice of each to garnish. Puree the kiwi and banana and blend in the apple juice and the buttermilk or yoghurt. Stir in a little mineral water if you like, pour into a glass and garnish with a little grated chocolate.

Papaya and Carrot

If you never thought of combining these two flavours you are in for a pleasant surprise as this blend is absolutely delightful.

Ingredients

1 serving

1/2 papaya, peeled and de-seeded

1 pear, peeled and cored

1 orange, juiced or squeezed

1 large carrot

Method

Scrub the carrot – no need to peel it – and juice. Juice the papaya and the pear, and squeeze or juice the orange. Combine all the juices in a glass and garnish with a slice of orange.

Italia

Basil, according to the 16th century apothecary John Gerard, 'taketh away sorrowfulness ... and maketh man merry and glad'. Basil certainly does help lift the spirits, it is also antiseptic and used across the Mediterranean as a remedy for pain relief for tension headaches, back and rheumatic pain. It goes particularly well with tomatoes, and this tasty mix combines the flavours of Italy and is a great lunchtime drink.

Ingredients

1 serving

$^1/_2$ bunch fresh basil – a few leaves reserved for garnish

2 tomatoes (or 1 big one!) or try 6–8 sweet, cherry tomatoes

100 ml (3 $^1/_2$ fl oz) live natural yoghurt

A little balsamic vinegar

A little olive oil

Seasoning to taste

Method

Wash and pat dry the basil and then strip off the leaves, keeping a few aside for garnish. Chop the rest of the leaves up finely. Juice the tomatoes, (or whizz them in a blender/food processor and pass the juice through a fine sieve) then puree the chopped basil leaves with the tomato juice and yoghurt. Season the mix to taste with a little olive oil, balsamic vinegar, salt and pepper, then pour into a glass and garnish with a few fresh basil leaves.

Pepper Power

Red peppers are higher in vitamins A and C than their green relatives – but the red bell pepper is simply a green pepper that has been allowed to mature and ripen, which is why it is sweeter in flavour. Low in calories, peppers are good sources of folic acid, fibre and potassium as well as the carotenoids betacarotene, lutein and zeaxanthin, which are believed to protect against muscular degeneration. Also important are the bioflavinoids with their powerful antioxidant properties in the fight against heart and circulatory disease.

Ingredients

1 serving

$^1/_2$ red pepper

1 large carrot

$^1/_4$ pineapple (or 3 slices canned pineapple in own juice, drained)

150 g (5 oz) grapes

Ground black pepper, or a sprinkle of cayenne pepper

Method

Wash and de-seed the pepper, wash the carrot – no need to peel – and peel the pineapple (if using fresh). Wash and de-stalk the grapes. Juice the pepper, the carrots, the pineapple and the grapes and combine the juices in a glass. Season with a little black pepper, or a sprinkle of cayenne if you prefer a little more spice in your life. Garnish with a slice of red pepper.

Vitaliser

A lovely blend of banana, blueberries and nectarine in a smooth yoghurt. Chilled, this is as nice as ice-cream! Blueberries contain the antibacterial anthocyanosides, which have a toning effect on the blood, while nectarines are virtually fat – and sodium – free making them ideal for anyone with high cholesterol levels or blood pressure problems. Pears are great for energy – and fresh pears contain a sugar based alcohol called sorbitol, which is a sugar free sweetener found in many processed 'tooth friendly' foods.

Ingredients

1 serving

1 small ripe banana

50 g (1 ³/₄ oz) blueberries

1 nectarine

1 small ripe pear

100 ml (3 ¹/₂ fl oz) live natural yoghurt

Splash of mineral water (optional)

Method

Peel the banana, wash the blueberries, wash and remove the stalk and core from the pear and wash and de-stone the nectarine. Keep a few berries and a slice or two of the other fruits for garnish. Juice the fruits and puree the banana in the fruit juice. Blend in the yoghurt. Pour into a glass and garnish with the reserved fruit.

Drive In

This is a power packed drink rich in magnesium to keep
your muscles working.

Ingredients

1 serving

1 small ripe banana

1 tomato – or 2–3 cherry
tomatoes

1 orange

$^1/_2$ grapefruit

$^1/_4$ small pineapple
or 2–3 slices of
canned fruit

Method

Peel and chop up the banana. Juice the
tomato, orange, grapefruit and pineapple
and puree the banana in the juices. Pour
into a glass and garnish with a slice of
orange or a cherry tomato.

Pick-Me-Up

A little chocolate to perk you up and bring a smile to your face.

Ingredients

1 serving

1 small ripe banana

100 ml (3 ¹/₂ fl oz) live, natural yoghurt

1 orange, squeezed or juiced

A little grated chocolate

Method

In a blender/food processor, puree the banana with the yoghurt and mix in the juice of the orange. Pour into a glass and dust with some grated chocolate. if you need an extra lift, add a teaspoon of honey into the blend.

Buttermilkshake

Real buttermilk can be hard to find, although some health and whole food stores do sell it – when they can source it. It is a natural by-product of butter churned from raw, unpasteurised cream. (Cultured buttermilk is pasteurised skim-milk inoculated with a lactic acid culture and then incubated). Thicker than regular milk, buttermilk, in spite of its name, is actually lower in fat. It has a tangy taste, like natural yoghurt, so, if you can't find buttermilk, substitute live yoghurt. You can make your own yoghurt very easily: see the recipe on page 49.

Ingredients

1 serving

100 ml (3 $\frac{1}{2}$ fl oz) buttermilk or natural, live yoghurt

$\frac{1}{4}$ small pineapple or 3 sliced canned fruit

75 g (2 $\frac{1}{2}$ oz) grapes

1 vanilla pod

1 cinnamon stick

Method

You can either juice the pineapple and grapes, or puree them in a food processor/blender. Mix the juices with the buttermilk or yoghurt. Slit the vanilla pod in half lengthways and scrape out the seeds with the point of a knife. Add them to the buttermilk/yoghurt mix and stir well. Pour into a large glass and garnish with the cinnamon stick.

Pineberries

This is a real fatigue zapper: iron rich raspberries and sweet pineapple will soon restore your energy levels.

Ingredients

1 serving

1/2 pineapple, or 4–6 slices of canned fruit

150 g (5 oz) raspberries

Method

Wash the raspberries and peel the pineapple. You can either juice the fruits, or whizz them together in a food processor/blender and then pass the juice through a fine sieve – although personally I love those little 'bits' of fruit! Stir the juices together over ice – try crushed ice for a really yummy slushy! Garnish with a few raspberries and a sprig of lemon balm or mint.

Mango Fix

Guaranteed to satisfy the craving for something sweet and give you
a real lift – but without the low immediately after snacking on something like
chocolate! Just the flowery aroma of juiced mango and pineapple is enough
to get you up and at it!

Ingredients

1 serving

1 mango

*½ pineapple, or 4–6 slices
canned fruit*

Method

*Cut the pineapple from the skin if using fresh,
and wash and de-stone the mango – you can
juice the skin or you can peel it if you prefer (or
if you are using a blender/food processor). Juice
the pineapple and the mango – or whizz the
two together in a blender/food processor – you
can pass the juices through a fine sieve if you
wish. Stir the juices together in a glass and
decorate with a piece of pineapple.*

Carrot, Spinach and Avocado

This spicy smoothie is great as a mid-afternoon 'pick-you-up', which will reinvigorate and refuel you for the rest of the day.

Ingredients

1 serving

3 carrots

5–7 fresh spinach leaves

$1/2$ avocado

Seasoning

Dash of Tabasco sauce (optional)

Method

Wash the carrots and the spinach, and pat dry. Juice the spinach, then the carrots and in a blender/food processor mix the juices with the avocado until smooth. Season to taste – and add a dash or two of Tabasco sauce to liven it all up if you like. Pour into a glass and garnish with some fresh parsley or a carrot stick stirrer.

Broccoli and Apple

This is a wonderfully balanced mix where the sweetness of the apple offsets the savoury broccoli, which is packed with Vitamins A, B complex and C, calcium, phosphorous, potassium, fibre, amino acids and protein. It's also low fat and low in calories but will get you through the afternoon – the hardest part of the day when your body is running low on 'fuel'.

Ingredients

1 serving

2 apples

4 broccoli florets

Method

Wash the broccoli and apple. Juice the broccoli, then the apple and combine the juices in a glass. Garnish with a slice of apple.

3 Cs

The 3 Cs in this peppery drink are (water) cress, carrots and cucumber. OK, so it's two Cs and a W but it's still a great way to combat tiredness during the day!

Ingredients

1 serving

1 large handful watercress

2 carrots

1/2 cucumber

Method

Scrub the carrot and cucumber – no need to peel – and rinse the watercress. Juice the watercress, then the carrots, and finally the cucumber, reserving a little for garnish. Mix the juices in a glass and garnish with a 'trail' of watercress and some cucumber.

Grape and Plum

This is simply lovely – it's also very refreshing and invigorating. Try it in the evening, if you're going out and not sure whether you will be dancing or dining. You'll have energy for a dance marathon, but won't want to overdo late night eating. This makes about 300 ml (about ½ pint); if you want less, cut the ingredient quantities by half.

Ingredients

1 serving
150 g (5 oz) red grapes
5 plums

Method

Juice the plums and the grapes and combine the juices in a glass – over a couple of ice cubes if you like. Garnish with a few grapes or a slice of plum – or both.

Powerpack

The name says it all! A gorgeous colour and a terrific taste.

Ingredients

1 serving

2 carrots

$^1/_2$ small beetroot –
about 70 g (2 oz) or so

1 orange

70 g (about 2 oz) strawberries,
with a few reserved for garnish

2–3 ice cubes

Method

*Juice the carrots, the beetroot and the orange.
Put the juices into a blender/food processor
with the strawberries and 2–3 ice cubes and
whizz together. Pour into a glass and garnish
with a strawberry and a slice of orange.*

Magnificent Seven

Seven fresh but simple ingredients make up this 'salad in a glass'. This is a great way to use up those left over odds and ends of vegetables. Be adventurous and inventive and vary the quantities and ingredients. For extra power, sprinkle with a few alfalfa sprouts or flax (linseeds), poppy or sesame seeds.

Ingredients

1 serving

1 carrot

$1/2$ green pepper, de-seeded

25g (1 oz) spinach

1 spring onion, chopped finely

1 celery stick

$1/4$ cucumber

1 small tomato

Seasoning to taste

Method

Wash the vegetables: there's no need to peel. Juice the carrot, pepper, spinach, celery stick, tomato and cucumber. Mix the juices in a glass, season to taste and sprinkle with the chopped spring onion.

Energy Burst

Drink your greens and say goodbye to fatigue!

Ingredients

1 serving

100 g (3 oz or so) spinach

1 large apple

$^1/_2$ yellow pepper, de-seeded

Method

Juice the spinach, the yellow pepper and the apple and combine the juices in a glass. Season with a little pepper if you like.

Autumn Fruits

Very simple to make and a delightful reviving flavour. This is a terrific way to beat the blues on dark mornings or afternoons in winter.

Ingredients

1 serving

2 apples

2 pears

$^1/_2$ grapefruit

Method

Juice the apples, the pears and the grapefruit. Combine in a glass – over ice if you like – and garnish with a little fruit.

Chocolate Shake

Introduced to Europe by Christopher Columbus, surprisingly it took more than 100 years for us to become 'addicted' to chocolate! Sometimes, nothing else will do. Yes, you could use carob – or St. John's Bread as it is called, since the Baptist managed in the wilderness on wild honey and locusts – the leguminous pods, which – when slowly roasted – are supposed to taste something like chocolate. Unlike chocolate, carob is caffeine free – so you won't get the 'hit' you get from the bean – but like chocolate it does contain tannic acid, which reduces the absorption of proteins. Some people like it, some are disappointed. Whichever you use, use it in moderation.

Ingredients

6 squares of chocolate: go for quality – a high cocoa content – rather than quantity!

2 scoops chocolate ice cream

250 ml (about 1/2 pint) full fat milk (don't even think about skinny milk!)

Whipped cream to decorate (if you must)

Method

Resisting all urges to eat it in one go, grate the chocolate – or melt it in a bowl over a saucepan of hot water. Put the milk, the chocolate, and the ice cream into a food processor/blender and whizz until the desired thickness is reached. You can, at this stage, throw in a banana or a few berries too! Pour into a tall glass, decorate with a good dollop of whipped cream – and perhaps a few sprinkles of grated chocolate – and serve with a straw. Enjoy it, get over it and move on!

Stress Busters

When we're calm and comfortable, stress is no problem. Stress is, in fact, part of everyday life, and the ways our bodies – and minds – have responded to stress have played a key role in humankind's survival. The 'primitive' 'flight or fight' response that our body produces 'automatically' when we are faced with danger is at the root of the stress problem: in our civilised societies, we don't get the chance to choose 'fight' or 'flight' to cope with stress, so the response the body makes is counterproductive. Our only option is to 'battle on', 'to grin and bear it', or 'grit our teeth'. As stress – and what we perceive to be stress – increases, stress induced illnesses increase. These illnesses include all sorts of complaints from the 'minor' to the deadly serious: insomnia, headaches, bad skin and hair days, asthma, high blood pressure, heart attacks.

Stress can affect our nutritional status too, which in turn aggravates stress-induced illnesses. For example, the over production of stomach acids can lead to inflamed stomach linings and ulcers, and at the other end of the digestive tract, stress can speed up the passage of food though the lower intestine and colon where many nutrients are absorbed and where the B vitamins are synthesised. Speeding up the process means food – and its nutriments – are not digested properly and fewer B vitamins – the very vitamins needed to keep the nervous system healthy – are synthesised.

The first steps to dealing with stress on the body is to deal with the causes of stress. This may mean major life changing decisions, or it may simply mean learning

to 'ease off' a little, not 'volunteering' to take on so much responsibility at work perhaps, or taking a short break. Yoga, Tai Chi, relaxation exercises, massage, aromatherapy – a little R & R – are all known to be beneficial for dealing with and releasing stress. And so too are certain foods.

To beat stress our bodies need lots of calming, soothing and spirit-lifting foods – that also taste really good. Enjoying what you eat or drink is vital: if you don't like the taste of something, you'll only get more stressed out! There are plenty of options available, so don't punish yourself!

When you're stressed, the last type of food you need is that which is stimulating, and top of the list is our old enemy, caffeine. Coffee, tea, chocolate, cola drinks (avoid the caffeine-free ones too as they contain so many artificial ingredients that you just don't need) and sports or 'energy' drinks – including the 'eye openers' on pages 50–78! – all contain caffeine. Ideally you should limit your caffeine intake to one or two cups a day. If you have been on the eight cups of coffee a day diet, then ease off slowly: you may find that too quick a withdrawal will lead to headaches and you'll feel more stressed than when you drank all that coffee!

High protein foods are high mental energy foods, so you need to avoid these. Instead, carbohydrate-rich foods are excellent sources of the amino acid tryptophan, which is converted by the body into seratonin, the mood-enhancing and calming hormone: bananas, pineapple, figs, tomatoes, avocados, dates, papayas and passion fruits.

Once again breakfast is the key meal in stress-busting: it should set you up for the day! It is also a good idea to do a little grazing through the day: don't go for more than two hours without a carbohydrate snack to keep your blood sugars level. Have a banana, or 1 or 2 dates.

The body's best way of dealing with stress is sleep. When you fall asleep the body begins to synthesise and utilise the nutrients in your food and starts its nightly maintenance and repair programme! Being hungry in the night – low blood sugar will not feed your brain to produce sleep-inducing hormones –

and of course, caffeine-laden drinks before bed, as well as stress, can all interrupt a good night's sleep.

There are lots of foods that can help promote a good night's sleep, especially those that contain the hormone seratonin – which induces sleep – and the starchy foods that contain tryptophan. The ancient Romans also believed in the power of lettuce: try the recipe for a Snoozing Rabbit on page 167.

Warning

If you are ill, have or suspect you may have an allergy or food intolerance, you need to consult a doctor. The recipes suggested are NOT substitutes for medical advice or prescribed medicines.

Banana Calmer

Soothe your mind and nourish nerves after a stressful day at work.

Ingredients

1 serving

250 ml (8 fl oz) milk

1 banana, peeled and sliced

2–3 ice cubes

1 teaspoon honey – or more
if you feel in need of an extra
bit of oomph!

1 pinch ground or
fresh grated nutmeg

Method

*Put all the ingredients into a blender/food
processor and whizz until smooth. Serve
with an extra pinch of nutmeg if you like.
Drink slowly – or sip through a straw.*

Creamy Mango

Did you know mangoes were related to cashew nuts! Full of vitamins A and C as well as calcium and potassium, mangoes are real energy boosters and help to stimulate the immune system. Bananas are also potassium rich and have vitamin B6, which balances the body's metabolism. Bananas also promote the release of seratonin – the body's natural 'happy' chemical, to lift your mood.

Ingredients

1 serving

1 mango, peeled and de-stoned

1 banana, peeled

1 orange, peeled

2–3 teaspoons grated/shredded coconut

Method

Place the mango, banana and coconut into a blender/food processor and whizz until smooth. Juice, squeeze, or simply pop the orange into the blender/food processor as well and whizz again. Serve and relax a while.

Smooth Serenity

Nourishing and calming, this sweet blend with a hint of spice will help stabilise the nerves, as well as help you to concentrate.

Ingredients

1 serving

$^1/_2$ tablespoon ground almonds

100 g (4 oz) dates, de-stoned

250 ml (about $^1/_2$ pint) rice milk

Good pinch ground ginger

Method

Put all the ingredients into a blender/food processor and whizz until smooth.

Banana and Coconut Milk

In the battles against stress, vitamins B and C, and the minerals zinc, potassium, calcium, magnesium and iron are important. Bananas and coconuts are both foods known to have a very calming effect on the nerves, while spices such as cinnamon and ginger are also well known as great stress relievers.

Ingredients

1 serving

2 large ripe bananas, peeled

250 ml (about ½ pint) coconut milk

Pinch of ground cinnamon

Method

Put the coconut milk and the bananas into a blender/food processor and whizz until smooth. Pour into a glass and sprinkle with a pinch of ground cinnamon.

Red Mist

'An apple a day keeps the doctor away' is the old proverb and the fruit has been long known to enhance immunity to infection and help ward off colds and flu. Beetroot and apples make a very pleasing and effective combination for boosting energy and immunity.

Ingredients

1 serving

1 small beetroot

2 apples

1/2 lemon

Method

Wash the beetroot and slice off the fibrous stalk at the bottom. Peel the lemon and chop the apple into chunks. Juice the beetroot, then the apples and then the lemon. Combine the juices in a glass and garnish with a slice of lemon.

Banana Fig

Figs are positively bursting with natural food energy – 55% sugars. They will give you a natural 'high' and provide carbohydrate, fibre and even a small amount of protein. Also in abundant levels in figs are calcium, magnesium, phosphorous and potassium!

Ingredients

1 serving

1 banana – peeled with a chunk reserved for garnish

1 fresh fig

100 ml (3 1/2 fl oz) buttermilk, or live natural yoghurt

1/2 vanilla pod

100 ml (3 1/2 fl oz) sparkling mineral water

Pinch of ground cinnamon

Ice cubes

Method

Chop the banana into chunks – keeping a piece for garnish. Cut open the fig and scoop out the flesh. Put the banana, fig and buttermilk, or live natural yoghurt into a blender/food processor and whizz until smooth. Cut a vanilla pod in half lengthwise, scrape out half of the seeds with the point of a knife and add them to the mixture. Whizz briefly again. Pour into a glass over ice cubes and top with sparkling mineral water. Garnish with the reserved banana – chopped into small pieces – and dust with a sprinkle of ground cinnamon.

Berry and Banana

Bananas with their creamy, smooth taste are a joy to drink, and, containing vitamin B6 and magnesium, they help keep nerves and muscles healthy. You can use any berries you like in this drink – blackberries, blueberries, raspberries, bilberries, cranberries, even Mammy Yokum's 'yokumberry' – L'il Abner never seemed to be stressed out!

Ingredients

1 serving

1 banana

150 g (3 ¹/₂ oz) berries of your choice

1 tablespoon ground almonds

150 ml (3 ¹/₂ fl oz) buttermilk, or live natural yoghurt

Mineral water (optional)

Pinch ground cinnamon

Method

Peel the banana and cut into chunks. Rinse the berries, remove any stalks and pat dry. Keep a few berries aside to garnish. Put the berries and the banana in a blender/food processor along with the ground almonds and buttermilk, or live natural yoghurt. If the mix is too thick, dilute with a splash of mineral water. Season with a pinch of ground cinnamon, pour into a large glass and garnish with the reserved berries.

Plum Yoghurt

Rich in folic acid, vitamin C and betacarotene, plums are great for boosting immunity. Folic acid is needed to guard against anaemia and irritability, confusion and memory loss, greying hair as well as gastrointestinal disorders – all the tangible signs of stress!

Ingredients

1 serving

4 plums, de-stoned

150 ml (3 ½ fl oz) natural live yoghurt

1 apple

Mineral water (optional)

Pinch ground cinnamon

Cinnamon stick (optional)

Method

Wash and de-stone the plums. Wash the apple and chop into chunks. Juice the plums and the apple – or if you prefer, puree the plums and apple in a blender/food processor. Add the yoghurt and blend together. If a little too thick, add a dash or two of mineral water. Pour into a glass and sprinkle with ground cinnamon and garnish with a cinnamon stick (optional).

Pineapple-Almond

A delicious way to beat stress and boost your energy levels.

Ingredients

1 serving

1 tbsp ground almonds

1 tbsp grated coconut

$^1/_4$ pineapple, peeled
(or 3 thick slices of
canned pineapple in own juice,
drained)

150 ml (3 $^1/_2$ fl oz)
natural live yoghurt

Method

Puree the almonds and coconut in a blender/food
processor with the juice of the pineapple (or you
can whizz it in a blender/food processor). Add the
yoghurt and blend again. Pour into a glass and
sprinkle with a little grated coconut if you like, or
a slice of pineapple – or try a chunk of pineapple
dipped into grated coconut!

Raspberry Buttermilk

This needs a little bit of preparation in advance, but it's well worth it! If you don't want to make frozen grape juice cubes, a few frozen or fresh berries instead make an equally delicious treat!

Ingredients

1 serving

about 40 g (1 oz) white grapes, juiced, or 25 ml (1 fl oz) white grape juice

75 g (2 ½ oz) raspberries

1 pear

100 ml (3 fl oz) buttermilk, or live natural yogurt

Chilled mineral water

A few grapes and raspberries for garnish – if you haven't already eaten them!

Method

Pour the grape juice into an ice cube tray and freeze for about 4 hours. Put the pear, the raspberries and the buttermilk, or live natural yogurt, in a blender/food processor and whizz until smooth. If too thick, dilute with a little chilled mineral water. Put the 'grape cubes' into a glass and pour over the buttermilk/natural yogurt shake. Serve in a glass and garnish with a few grapes or berries.

Orange Pear

A very simple and delicious drink guaranteed to help you unwind and de-stress.

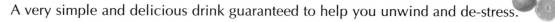

Ingredients

1 serving

3 oranges

1 pear

Method

Peel the oranges and remove the stalk from the pear. Cut into chunks and juice – or whizz in a blender/food processor. Pour into a glass over ice and garnish with a slice of orange.

Super Stress Buster

A tangy cocktail of vitamins C and B to unwind with at the end of the day.

Ingredients

1 serving

1 broccoli floret

1 tomato

$\frac{1}{2}$ red pepper

1 carrot

1 stalk of celery

Small bunch of parsley

1 celery stalk for stirring it all up with!

Method

Juice the broccoli, then the $\frac{1}{2}$ red pepper, the carrot, the celery, the parsley and the tomato. Blend the juices together in a glass and garnish with a sprig of parsley and a celery stalk.

Panic attack

Our skin is often the first to suffer when we are under stress, so keep it looking good with this combo. Apricots and peaches are high in vitamin A – which is why cosmetic companies value them for their skin care properties.

Ingredients

1 serving

2 apples

3 apricots (if using dried, rehydrate them by soaking or 'cooking' in a little water)

1 peach

Method

Juice the apricots, peach and the apple. Combine the juices in a tall glass – over ice if you like – and garnish with a slice of peach.

Raspberry Nectar

Rich in vitamin B, this tasty drink will 'de-frazzle' nerves and give a well deserved boost to both body and spirit – especially when you smell the lovely scents of fruit and lemon balm or mint.

Ingredients

1 serving

175 g (6 oz) raspberries

2 peaches

Sprig mint or lemon balm

Method

Rinse and juice the raspberries. De-stone the peaches and cut into quarters. Juice the peaches and pour into a glass with the raspberry juice. Garnish with some raspberries, a slice of peach and a sprig of mint or lemon balm. You can make this in a blender/food processor as well: just whizz the fruits and then blend the juices.

Snoozing Rabbit

One of the most frequently suffered effects of stress is insomnia. A bad night's sleep (or day's sleep if you are a shift worker) carries over fatigue and stress to the next day. Try this lettuce lovely before bed – remember how Peter Rabbit fell asleep in Mr. McGregor's garden....!

Ingredients

1 serving

3 carrots

$^1/_2$ head of lettuce

Method

Scrub the carrots – no need to peel – and rinse and pat dry the lettuce leaves. Juice them up and blend them in a tall glass.

Celery, Lettuce and Cucumber

When counting sheep only keeps you awake, try this bedtime calmer.

Ingredients

1 serving

3 stalks of celery

$^1/_2$ small lettuce

$^1/_2$ cucumber

Method

Rinse the vegetables and pat dry. Juice them and combine in a tall glass, garnished with a slice of cucumber or two.

Celery, Carrot and Cress

Celery and watercress contain magnesium, which calms the nervous system. The carrots add a touch of sweetness and volume, making this a great 'supper snack' that will help you wind down, sleep and wake bright and fresh.

Ingredients

1 serving

2 carrots

2 stalks of celery

1 handful of watercress

Method

Wash the veggies – no need to peel the carrots – and juice the ingredients. Combine the juices in a tall glass and garnish with a sprig of watercress, or a celery stalk to munch on.

Salad Soup

Going to bed on an empty stomach can be as bad as going to bed 'too full'. If it's late and you're a bit peckish, try this 'soup': it's light but nourishing and all those lovely vitamins and minerals will be hard at work while you snooze gently on!

Ingredients

1 serving

3 tomatoes

1/2 lettuce

5 cm (2 in) cucumber

Small handful of parsley

1/2 lemon

Method

Rinse the veggies and juice the lettuce, followed by the tomatoes, the cucumber and the parsley. Peel the lemon and then juice 1/2 of it. Combine the juices in a glass, garnish with a sprig or two of parsley – nature's 'breath freshener' – and sip slowly.

Power Booster

Being exhausted and run down when going to bed puts a great deal of strain on your body through the night. You may be asleep, but your body is still hard at work, cleansing, synthesising vitamins and minerals, pumping oxygen and blood around and trying to do the best job it can to 'heal' and keep infections at bay. Boost your body's power, cleanse and nourish at bedtime with this light purple cocktail.

Ingredients

1 serving

2 apples

100 g (4 oz) white grapes

50 g (2 oz) beetroot

1 cm (¹/₂ in) slice
of fresh ginger

Method

Wash, chop and juice the apples. Chop the beetroot and juice it. Juice the ginger and then combine all the juices in a glass. Garnish with a few grapes.

Looking Good, Feeling Great

Keeping our bodies in tip top condition, full of energy and 'get up and go' is not the only reason for enjoying fruits and vegetables. Looking good is also important. It's one of those cycles: if you feel good, you'll look good too, and, if you look good, you'll feel good. The 'inner' and 'outer' health of our bodies are closely related: the outer appearance is the visible manifestation of our health.

To feel good and look good means achieving a balanced state of health and vitality. We need nutrients to provide us with the raw materials to maintain every function in our body. The nervous system needs vitamins B and C, calcium and magnesium to ensure we cope with the stress in our daily lives and help us keep 'on top of things' – to keep a balanced perspective: not so huge as to become hysterical, not so calm as to be unresponsive! The immune system needs to be supported to prevent, fight and recover from infections, with food rich in vitamins A, B, C and E, calcium, magnesium, iron, zinc and selenium. And we need our digestive systems to be working efficiently to break down and assimilate all these nutrients, and to get rid of waste.

While the fantastic health giving properties of fresh fruits, vegetables, herbs and spices can be put to wonderful use, these alone won't work miracles! We need to take regular exercise to improve our circulation – to get oxygen to each and every cell and tissue in the body. Exercise needs to balance with rest and relaxation to allow our bodies to recover from exertion and to 'recharge'. With careful consideration of our diet – our 'way of life' – good skin free of spots, dryness and blemishes, bright eyes, shining hair, strong teeth and nails and a body that moves freely with grace and ease, can be achieved.

Our body weight is also closely connected to our health: being overweight can not only contribute to a range of health problems like diabetes, high blood pressure and heart disease but it also affects how we 'feel' about ourselves. Our weight can affect our confidence and, consequently, we can feel less positive about our 'value' in the world. The best way to lose weight is naturally: combining healthy eating – not starving your body but nourishing it with good things – with regular exercise.

The recipes in this section are not designed for weight loss, but by increasing your intake of fresh produce that is tasty, satisfying and nutritious, don't be surprised if you do start feeling more energetic and you start wanting to burn off more calories with some exercise – or by dancing the night away!

A quick glance along the shelves of 'beauty products' – cleansers, toners, masks, exfoliants, scrubs, astringents, and so on will reveal just how important vitamins and minerals are to the manufacturers of cosmetics: vitamin C helps to build collagen and elastin, which helps keep the skin free from wrinkles. Forget botox, eat cherries instead! Vitamins A and D are added to many cosmetic and beauty products to help maintain soft skin and repair body tissues along with vitamin E to stop the ageing process. These three fat soluble vitamins, when combined with vegetable oils, are absorbed through the skin and released internally. The very small quantities available in a pot of 'beauty cream' are ounce for ounce probably more expensive than covering ourselves in gold leaf! While no girl – and many boys – will ever deny the psychological benefit of a little retail therapy, the most effective way to get your vitamins and improve your skin is by eating and drinking! But if you do find yourself with a little leftover avocado, mash it up and slap it on your face!

When nails split or break it is annoying, but if it happens regularly it may be because you are deficient in minerals: white spots on the nails are a sign of zinc deficiency, while lack of iron makes for brittle nails. These minerals are found in abundance in fresh fruit and vegetables, but remember that iron is best assimilated when there is vitamin C available.

If you're having more than your fair share of 'bad hair days', then you need to boost your vitamin B intake:

manufacturers of hair care products have long recognised the value of all the B-complex vitamins in their products as they stimulate the scalp, thicken hair and aid in the prevention of baldness by stimulating hair growth. Look on bottles for the ingredients panthotenic acid, inositol, choline, folic acid and PABA (para-aminobenzoic acid) and you're looking at B-complex vitamins! The B-complex vitamins are water soluble, which means they can't be stored in the body but are 'washed' out in the urine. Consequently, these 'busy-bs' need to be replaced daily. Don't bother washing your hair daily to improve it, boost your vitamin B intake and start to see – and feel – the difference in your hair!

We all remember being told to eat our carrots so we could see in the dark – and whoever told us that was right. Night-blindness is more often than not caused by a vitamin A deficiency, which can be remedied by simply eating 3 small carrots a day. Carrots, like all yellow and orange foods, such as apricots, mangoes and peppers, as well as leafy green vegetables like spinach, watercress and spring greens, are high in betacarotene, which is cleverly converted in our bodies into vitamin A. A few carrot sticks or a delicious, freshly juiced carrot (combined perhaps with a juiced apple), is a great

way to put a sparkle in your eyes. Blueberries, cranberries and citrus fruits will help to maintain circulation to and from the eyes and strengthen the fine capillaries, thereby slowing the problem of the deteriorating eyesight that accompanies the ageing process. These foods will also help ward off infections that cause styes and conjunctivitis.

Warning

If you are ill, have or suspect you may have an allergy or food intolerance, you need to consult a doctor. The recipes suggested are NOT substitutes for medical advice or prescribed medicines!

Natural Beauty

Those 'old wives' were right: You are what you eat. So why not be a natural beauty? Apples are a good source of vitamin C, are rich in soluble fibre and pectin, which help eliminate cholesterol and fight off environmental pollutants, including heavy metals like lead and mercury. The smell of apples alone can lower blood pressure! Cantaloupe melons, with their high levels of carotenoids, may inhibit the growth of cancer cells and help maintain the health of body tissues, including the skin.

Ingredients

1 serving

2 apples

¹/₂ cantaloupe melon

Method

Wash and chop the apples. Wash the rind of the melon – there's no need to remove it, although you may prefer to remove both the skin and the seeds. Juice the fruits and combine in a glass. Garnish with a slice of apple if you like.

Papaya Power

Very simple to make – and fast too – which makes it a great drink if you're too busy to breakfast properly. The natural sugars in the papaya will keep you energised until you can take a mid-morning break.

Ingredients
1 serving

1 papaya, peeled and de-seeded

$1/2$ lemon

Method

In a blender/food processor, puree the papaya with the juice of half a lemon. Pour into a glass, sit down and relax for a few minutes while you enjoy this drink.

Tomato and Watercress

A bit spotty? Then tomato juice laced with peppery watercress is an excellent 'detoxifier' for the skin. It will also stabilise hormones with the zinc that is present in both tomatoes and watercress.

Ingredients

1 serving

4 ripe tomatoes

Large handful of watercress

Bunch of parsley

Juicer Method

Wash the tomatoes and chop into chunks. Rinse and juice the watercress and parsley, then the tomatoes and blend in a glass. Garnish with a cherry tomato and a sprig of parsley.

Blender Method

Wash the tomatoes and chop into chunks. Rinse and chop the parsley and watercress. Put all the ingredients into a blender/food processor and whizz together until smooth.

Raspberry Rinse

Dry skin? Oily Skin? Raspberries are rich in zinc, which helps to regulate the activity of the sebaceous glands. Melon is a terrific detoxifier and will help sweep away toxins in your system.

Ingredients

1 serving

150 g (5 oz) raspberries

$1/4$ cantaloupe melon

1 apple

Method

Wash the apple and chop into chunks. Rinse the raspberries. Skin (and de-seed if you wish) the melon and chop the flesh into chunks. Juice the berries, then the apple and then the melon. Combine the juices in a tall glass – over ice if you like. Garnish with a few raspberries and a slice of apple if you like.

Melon aid

Melons are soothing and cooling – ideal for relieving the itchiness of eczema or the excesses of the sun.

Ingredients

1 serving

$\frac{1}{2}$ yellow melon

Sparkling mineral water

Mint sprig

Method

Juice the melon flesh and seeds. Pour into a tall glass – over ice if you like – and top with sparkling mineral water. Garnish with a sprig of mint.

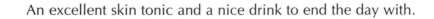

Apple Glow

An excellent skin tonic and a nice drink to end the day with.

Ingredients

1 serving

1 apple

$\frac{1}{2}$ yellow melon

100 g (4 oz) red grapes

$\frac{1}{2}$ lemon

Method

Remove the pips – and the skin if you wish – from the melon. Chop the apple into chunks, and rinse the grapes. Peel the lemon. Juice all the fruits and combine in a glass. Garnish with a slice of lemon or a few grapes.

Chinese Cherry Tea

Vitamin C builds collagen and elastin, which keeps those wrinkles at bay, while vitamin A keeps it supple. Both these are to be found in cherries, as well as calcium (for strong teeth and bones!) magnesium, potassium and iron. The cherry blossom in spring is for the Chinese, a symbol of youth and feminine beauty, but the delicious, power-packed fruit is a good enough reason to enjoy it!

Ingredients

1 serving

75 g (3 oz) of cherries, stoned and stalk removed

1 teaspoon honey

$^1/_2$ lemon, juiced

300 ml ($^1/_2$ pint) boiling water

Method

Place the cherries, honey and lemon juice in a blender/food processor and pour on the boiling water. Whizz the ingredients together and pour into a heat proof glass or cup. Float some slices of lemon on top if you like. Sip slowly.

Sun Block

Lots of betacarotene to protect the skin, this is a 'great skin' drink for summer.

Ingredients

1 serving

½ mango

¼ pineapple, skin removed

2 carrots, scrubbed but not peeled

1 apple

Ice cubes

Method

Peel the mango and cut off a slice for garnish. Chop up the flesh and juice it. Juice the pineapple, the carrots and the apple. Combine the juices in a tall glass – over ice if you like – and garnish with the mango slice.

Mango and Grape

Red grapes contain a substance called resveratol, a potential anticarcinogenic. They also have B3, B6, biotin, magnesium, potassium, phosphorous, copper, iron, selenium and zinc, making these juicy fruits excellent free-radical hunters and detoxifiers, especially of the skin. Mango is a good source of A, C and E – all those vitamins cosmetic companies try to get into their face creams!

Ingredients

1 serving

1 mango, peeled and de-stoned

150 g (5 oz) red grapes

Method

Cut the mango in half and ease out the stone. Remove the peel and juice the flesh. Rinse the grapes and juice them. Combine the juices in a glass and garnish with fruit. You can make this drink easily in a blender/food processor too: simply whizz the fruits together!

Apple, Celery and Alfalfa

Psoriasis is a relatively common skin condition that often 'runs in families'. Sunlight and sea water are excellent for both preventing and relieving troublesome skin conditions – that's why we always look so good after a relaxing vacation! Put a little sunshine inside yourself with this refreshing apple based drink – and celery is good for the nerves too!

Ingredients

1 serving

1 green apple

1 celery stalk

Small handful of alfalfa sprouts

Method

Juice the celery, the apple and the alfalfa sprouts – reserving a few for garnish. Combine the juices in a glass and sprinkle the alfalfa sprouts on top.

Apple-Beet

Both beetroot and apples are renowned for their cleansing properties. Because they aid the digestion and absorption of vitamins and minerals, beetroots and apples are useful in restoring skin to glowing health.

Ingredients

1 serving

½ small beetroot

2 apples

Slice of lemon or lime

Method

Wash the beetroot and the apples and cut into chunks. Juice them, combine the juices in a glass and garnish with a slice of lemon or lime.

Broccoli, Pear and Pineapple

Broccoli is a useful aid in detox and boosts energy and strength. With A, C, and E among its many qualities, it's a bonus for the skin. Cooling and calming pears, along with sweet pineapple, help speed up tissue repair, while Savoy cabbage is a good source of vitamins A, C and B3, which help keep the skin healthy.

Ingredients

1 serving

100 g (3$\frac{1}{2}$ oz) broccoli florets

$\frac{1}{4}$ pineapple

1 pear

$\frac{1}{4}$ small Savoy cabbage

Pinch ground ginger

Method

Wash the broccoli, and remove the skin from the pineapple. Juice the ingredients, combine in a glass and sprinkle with the pinch of ground ginger.

Pink Pineapple

Lovely – what more can I say?!

Ingredients

1 serving

¼ pineapple

1 orange – a blood orange will add an even deeper colour!

150 g (5 oz) strawberries

Method

Peel the pineapple and the orange – keep a slice for garnish if you like. Wash the strawberries and remove the stalks. Eat at least one strawberry (they are irresistible!) and put one aside for garnish! Juice the pineapple, the strawberries and the oranges. Combine the juices in a glass – over ice if you like – and garnish with a strawberry and a slice of lemon.

Broccoli, Carrot and Cucumber

Broccoli is not the nicest juice – but the sweetness of the carrots and the refreshing coolness of the cucumber do help. It's a really good combination for dealing with skin 'problems' brought on by stress, overwork and pollution.

Ingredients

1 serving

1 small cucumber

4 broccoli florets

1 carrot

Seasoning to taste

Method

Scrub the carrot and the cucumber – no need to peel. Juice the broccoli, then the carrot and finally the cucumber. Stir the juices together, season to taste and garnish with a slice of cucumber.

Heights of Passion

A good source of vitamins A and C, the punchy flavour of passion fruit is hard to resist. Don't worry about the seeds, they're edible too! Mixed with yoghurt into a smoothie, it's a really 'posh pudding'!

Ingredients

1 serving

2 passion fruits

1 orange

$^1/_2$ lime

150 ml (3 $^1/_2$ fl oz)
natural live yoghurt

Sparkling mineral water
(optional)

Method

Scoop the flesh from the passion fruits. Squeeze the orange and lime – or peel and pop in a blender/food processor with the passion fruit and whizz together. Add the yoghurt and whizz again briefly. Pour into a glass. You can dilute with sparkling mineral water and serve over ice if you prefer a longer drink.

Mr. Green

Surprise yourself with this combination of broccoli and grapes – it's actually quite delicious and really good for your skin.

Ingredients

1 serving

150 g (5 oz) green grapes

150 g (5 oz) broccoli florets – 4–5 is about right!

Sprig of mint

Method

Juice the broccoli and the grapes. Combine the juices in a glass and garnish with a sprig of fresh mint.

Speckled Tom

A really herby drink – you can add a dash of Worcestershire sauce if you like. Parsley contains as much vitamin A as cod liver oil and three times as much vitamin C as oranges – so eat your garnish! In France basil is known as *l'herbe royale* (the royal herb). It is antiseptic and said to be a relief for acne! It is also a mild sedative, so this makes a nice late evening snack!

Ingredients

1 serving

6 tomatoes

6 fresh basil leaves

Handful of fresh parsley

Method

Juice or whizz the tomatoes in a blender/food processor. Finely chop the basil and parsley – keep a sprig for garnish and stir into the tomato juice.

Kale and Hearty

Curly kale deserves to be far more popular than it is. It has all the anticancer properties of the brassica family but with a huge amount of betacarotene – 100 g (3 ½ oz) provides a whole day's dose for a woman! It is also a superior source of vitamin A, calcium, and iron. Wheatgrass, when juiced, is high in calcium, potassium, chlorophyll and magnesium, and it's also surprisingly sweet! Because the flavours are quite strong, and take a bit of getting used to, this recipe is for a small serving.

Ingredients

1 serving of about 2 fl oz

25 g (1 oz) curly kale

100g (3 ½ oz) wheatgrass
(if you can't get it 'whole',
many juice bars and health food
stores sell it ready juiced

Method

Juice the curly kale and the wheatgrass (or mix the two juices). Combine in a glass.

Very-Berry

This ruby red juice of raspberries and cranberries is just gorgeous – a perfect sweet-sour balance and bursting with goodness. It's a combination that's reputed to be great for the skin – and can be especially helpful if you are a bit acne prone.

Ingredients

1 serving

150 g (5 oz) cranberries

150 g (5 oz) raspberries

Ice

Sprig of mint
or lemon balm

Method

Juice the berries – keeping a few for garnish – or whizz them in a blender/food processor. Pour over ice, garnish with the saved fruit and add a sprig of mint or lemon balm.

Popeyes Sundowner

O.J. – but with muscles! A super source of vitamin A (plus iron of course), spinach is also higher in protein than most vegetables. Mixed here with lots of orange juice, this is a great way to 'eat your greens' without noticing them! Bioflavinoids found in the pith and segment 'walls' of citrus fruits strengthen the walls of the tiny blood capillaries, helping to avoid collapse – and broken veins appearing on the surface of your skin. You can try this recipe too with grapefruits, clementines or satsumas – or all of them!

Ingredients

2 oranges
6 spinach leaves

Method

Peel the orange, leaving on as much pith as you can to get at those bioflavinoids. Juice the spinach and the oranges and combine the juices in a glass. Decorate with a wedge of orange and serve with a straw!

Carrot, Celery and Rosemary

Carrots detoxify and help maintain good circulation, while rosemary – long famous for its reputation for improving the memory – also stimulates blood flow to the head, so it's good for headaches and is supposed to keep dandruff and grey hair at bay!

Ingredients

1 serving

1 large carrot

2 celery stalks

3 soft sprigs of rosemary

Pepper to taste

Method

Wash the carrots, celery, rosemary and juice. Blend the juices together and season with pepper. Drink straight away.

Raspberry Sunrise

Suck a raspberry to soothe a sore throat or a mouth ulcer! And, according to Chinese medicine, these lovely berries can also improve your sexual appetite! Tangerines, although 'milder' than oranges, are rich in vitamin B1 (thiamine), which helps maintain healthy hair follicles. Put them together and you'll feel like you're glowing – inside and out!

Ingredients

2 servings – to share with a loved one!

400 g (1 lb) raspberries

6 tangerines

Method

Juice each fruit or whizz the fruits together in a blender/food processor. Serve in a pair of tall glasses and feel a raspberry ripple!

Cherry Blossom

Rejuvenating, detoxifying, and antioxidant, sweet cherries are positively bursting with goodness including vitamins A and B2 (riboflavin), betacarotene, potassium, calcium and phosphorous. Mix with orange juice for extra vitamin C and a lovely long drink.

Ingredients

1 serving

4 oranges

1 good handful –
12–15 cherries

Method

Peel the orange, leaving on as much pith as possible. Rinse the cherries and de-stone them – a bit fiddly but worth it! Juice the cherries and oranges, combine in a glass and garnish with a slice of orange and a cherry. You can make this in a blender/food processor too: if you're not keen on 'bits' of skin or pith, simply strain the juices through a fine sieve, but remember, those 'bits' are full of goodness!

Kwik-kiwi-fix

The strength of zinc (in raspberries) and B2 (riboflavin) in kiwis make this a power drink for strong hair, nails – and gums too!

Ingredients
1 serving
2 kiwis

125 g (4 oz) raspberries

Ice cubes (optional)

Method
Peel the kiwis. Pop the kiwis and the raspberries (keeping a few aside for garnish) into the juicer – or into a blender/food processor and whizz them. Pour the juices into an ice filled glass and garnish with the raspberries – if you haven't already eaten them!

Carrot and Apple

It is said that 'the eyes are the windows of the soul' and nothing looks better than clean, sparkling windows – on a house or in the head! So simple and so delicious, and when did you last see a rabbit wearing spectacles?

Ingredients

1 serving

2 apples

1 big carrot

Method

Wash the carrot and the apples. Cut into chunks. Juice them and combine the juices in a tall glass.

Rescue Remedies

Making sensible food choices not only keeps our energy levels topped up, but our immune system ready and on the alert for infections and diseases. It is also widely thought that some foods can target specific complaints and diseases. Nevertheless, there are times when we all succumb to a cold or flu, have aches and pains, or suffer from a common ailment.

Although we are constantly surrounded by cold viruses, when our immune systems are strong, we don't catch them! Too often we get the first symptoms – a runny nose, a sore throat, a headache and a general feeling of being a 'bit under the weather' – and reach for the medicine cabinet. In all instances, prevention is better than cure: we can protect ourselves quite easily from common colds and flu by strengthening our body's resistance to them. Because some fruit and vegetables have high antioxidant contents, juices are excellent in helping prevent colds and flu. The 'super foods' to help ward off colds and foods are those with high vitamin C content such as citrus fruits, but also those that help to cleanse the body of toxins and stimulate the immune system and the production of antibodies: apples, carrots, beetroot, and cabbage are among those fruits and vegetables in the 'food pharmacy'. Zinc has also been shown to be beneficial in combating colds and the best natural and fresh sources to help you on the road to feeling better are raspberries, tomatoes, blackcurrants and broccoli.

Scientific analysis of the properties of foodstuffs continues to discover exactly what components are beneficial in healing our bodies. In many cases, modern research is reinforcing ancient folk cures. 'An apple a day, keeps the doctor away' but two a day could be a real tonic for the heart and the circulation. We know that the pectin (the soluble fibre) helps the body to eliminate cholesterol. And long used as an accompaniment to 'heavy meats' like pork, it's the malic and tartaric acid in apples that aids digestion. Cherries were highly prized by the ancient Greek physicians but we know that the ellagic acid inhibits carcinogenic cells. Blackberries were used in traditional medicine as a relief for gout, and now we know their high vitamin E content makes them useful in preventing heart disease.

While we often blame modern life for many ills, we must also thank it for bringing us new foods – and new medicines: pineapples from Hawaii with their protein digesting enzyme bromelain; bananas from Africa and the Caribbean, packed full of potassium, B6 and folic acid; papayas, originally natives of southern Mexico and Costa Rica, with their betacarotene (which is an antioxidant and converted in the body into vitamin A), as well as avocados (from Peru), and kiwi fruits (originally from China) are just a handful of exciting tastes we can now enjoy and benefit from year round.

The identification of phtyonutrients – the organic components of plants that are believed to promote good health in humans – has led to a greater understanding of how we can harness fresh fruits and vegetables to protect physical well being. Compounds such as carotenoids – the red, orange, and yellow pigments that colour many fruits and vegetables – appear to protect the body

against some cancers, heart diseases and muscular degeneration. With their antioxidant properties, they seek out and destroy the harmful free radicals in cells that are known to cause certain diseases.

In this section, a selection of delicious fruit and vegetable drinks is offered as reliefs for some of the most common ailments such as cystitis, the symptoms of PMS and to help the digestive system cope with indigestion, flatulence and constipation. In short, recipes to help boost your immune system, cleanse the body of toxins, boost your energy levels, get you back on your feet and most of all, offer you some delicious, nutritious treats.

Warning

If you are ill, have or suspect you may have an allergy or food intolerance, you need to consult a doctor. The recipes suggested are NOT substitutes for medical advice or prescribed medicines.

Avocado Calmer

A smooth creamy drink that should satisfy those food cravings – 'the attack of the munchies' – and for those who suffer from PMS, avocados are great as they are high in vitamins B and E (good for the hormones) and at the same time, calming on the nervous system.

Ingredients

1 serving

1 ripe avocado, peeled and sliced

1 clove of garlic, peeled (optional)

½ lemon, squeezed

300 ml (about ½ pint) rice milk

Seasoning to taste

Sprig fresh coriander to garnish

Method

Put the avocado into a blender/food processor with the garlic clove (optional), the lemon juice and the rice milk and blend until smooth. Season to taste, pour into a glass and garnish with a sprig of fresh coriander.

Orange and Cress

A peppery-orange blend that is full of nutriments. It will boost energy levels to get you through those dark days if you're suffering from PMS.

Ingredients

1 serving
4 oranges
Large bunch watercress

Method

Rinse the watercress and peel the oranges. Juice the watercress, then the oranges and then combine the juices in a glass. Garnish with a slice of orange.

Peppery Apples

The sweetness of the apples is offset with the peppery taste of the watercress. Green peppers are full of vitamin B6 (pyridoxine,) which helps to reduce water retention.

Ingredients

1 serving

1 green pepper
3 apples
Small handful watercress

Method

Remove the top and the seeds from the green pepper, rinse the watercress and wash and chop the apples. Keep a sprig of watercress aside for garnish. Juice the pepper, followed by the watercress, then the apples. Combine the juices in a glass–over ice is nice–and garnish with the sprig of watercress.

Kiwipear

If you're on a bit of a hormone roller coaster try this delightful green juice packed with essential trace minerals to help you stay on the rails.

Ingredients

1 serving
2 kiwis
2 pears

Method

Peel the kiwis and juice them. Chop the pears and juice them too. Stir the juices together in a tall glass and garnish with a slice or two of fruit.

Melon and Strawberry Frolic

A gorgeous drink – and full of folic acid too, which is needed to counter anaemia. It's also good for irritability, gastrointestinal disturbances and stopping your hair from going grey!

Ingredients

1 serving

½ yellow melon

100 g (4 oz) strawberries

Method

Remove the seeds and the skin from the melon. Cut the flesh into chunks. Rinse and hull the strawberries and juice them. Juice the melon and blend the juices in a glass.

Fruity Fantasy

Help your digestion and boost your metabolism with this striking combo.

Ingredients

1 serving
⅛ Savoy cabbage
¼ pineapple
2 apples
Sprig of mint

Method

Wash and juice the cabbage. Peel and juice the pineapple. Wash and juice the apples. Mix the juices well in a glass. Garnish with a little fruit and a sprig of fresh mint.

Carrot and Ginger

Excellent for the digestion, carrots are naturally sweet but here a little ginger – used for centuries to ease nausea – adds a 'zing' to the flavour.

Ingredients

1 serving

4 carrots

2 cm (¾ in) piece
of fresh ginger

Method

Scrub the carrots – no need to peel them – and chop to fit into your juicer. Peel the ginger and juice. Combine the juices in a glass and sip slowly.

Spiced Melon

If you are pregnant and suffering from morning sickness – or even if you're not pregnant and are feeling a little queasy – this blend of melon and ginger is great for settling the stomach. Add some sparkling mineral water if you prefer a longer drink.

Ingredients

1 serving

½ yellow melon

2 cm (¾ in) piece of fresh ginger

Sparkling mineral water (optional)

Method

Scoop out the seeds and remove the skin from the melon. Peel the ginger and juice the ingredients. Mix in a tall glass, top with sparkling mineral water if you wish and sip slowly.

Apple Spritzer

Overdid the spicy or greasy food last night? Apples are the simple but effective remedy, but if you have diarrhoea, dilute with a little more mineral water.

Ingredients

1 serving

2 apples

50 ml (1 ¼ fl oz) sparkling mineral water, or more if needed

Method

Wash and chop the apples and feed into the juicer. Mix with sparkling mineral water to taste.

Way to Go

Well known as an 'intestinal sweeper' prunes are also a good source of iron, calcium, magnesium and phosphorous. Pears cool and calm a nervous, acid or inflamed digestive system and, like spinach, are also slightly diuretic.

Ingredients

1 serving

1 small pear

12.5 g (½ oz) – about 2 pitted prunes

75 g (2 oz) spinach

Ice cubes

Method

Juice all the ingredients and serve in a glass over ice, garnished with a slice of pear if you like.

Beet and Carrot Sweep

Nourish and cleanse at the same time: beetroot stimulates the liver and bowel functions, enhancing the elimination of wastes and toxins, while carrots soothe the lining of the gut.

Ingredients

1 serving
3 carrots
½ small beetroot
Coriander leaves to garnish

Method

Scrub the carrots – no need to peel – and the beet and chop into chunks. Juice the carrots and beetroot. Blend the juices together in a glass, garnished with a spring of coriander.

Banana and Almond Regulator

Bananas and almonds are fibre rich foods that promote normal bowel function, but they are also 'calming' foods when constipation is the result of, or is exacerbated by, nervous tension. Oranges have a gentle laxative effect, while the natural live yoghurt will help maintain a healthy balance of 'good bacteria' in the gut.

Ingredients

1 serving

1 banana, peeled and chopped

25 g (1 oz) ground almonds

1 orange, juiced or squeezed

150 ml (3 ½ fl oz)
natural, live yoghurt

1 teaspoon honey (optional)

Pinch ground nutmeg

Method

Place the banana and ground almonds into a blender/food processor with the orange juice, the yoghurt, and the honey (optional) and whizz until smooth and creamy. Pour into a glass and garnish with a dusting of ground nutmeg.

Spinach Shifter

A lack of fibre or a diet high in over-processed foods, too little exercise, and stress can cause constipation – and misery. Instead of reaching for the medicine cabinet and an over-the-counter remedy (which can strip your body of minerals and vitamins), try the 'food pharmacy' instead: all fresh juices will relax the bowels, but leafy green vegetables, which are rich in minerals, will help maintain a healthy balance.

Ingredients

1 serving
3 tomatoes
3 large spinach leaves
1 carrot

Method

Rinse the spinach and scrub the carrot – no need to peel. Juice the spinach, then the carrot and then the tomatoes. Combine all the juices in a glass, garnished with a sprig of parsley if you like.

Caribbean Cure

Indigestion can be very painful but this blend of tropical fruits will do the trick: coconut milk is famous for relieving acidity, pineapple is anti-inflammatory and contains bromelain to help balance stomach acids, while juicy papaya cools and breaks down protein to help your own stomach enzymes digest food.

Ingredients

1 serving

½ ripe papaya, peeled and de-seeded

¼ pineapple, peeled and cut into chunks (or three slices of canned pineapple)

300 ml (½ pint) coconut milk

Still or sparkling mineral water (optional)

Pinch ground nutmeg

Method

Put the papaya, pineapple and coconut milk into a blender/food processor and whizz them together until smooth. If a little too thick, add a splash of mineral water. Pour into a glass and dust with a pinch of ground nutmeg and sip slowly.

Gas Station

Grapefruit will help digest those starchy foods and fats and help sweep waste and toxins from the bowels. The mango and pineapple too will help. Together this is a refreshing way to calm high winds!

Ingredients

1 serving

1 ripe mango, peeled and sliced

¼ pineapple, peeled, or three slices canned pineapple

½ pink grapefruit, juiced or squeezed

Fresh lemon balm or mint to garnish

Method

Put the mango, the pineapple and the grapefruit juice into a blender/food processor and whizz until smooth. Pour into a glass and garnish with a sprig of lemon balm or mint.

Calmer

The occasional occurrence of diarrhoea can be debilitating – and upsetting.
It's actually your body trying really hard to get rid of something that's
upsetting it. Ideally, you should let it 'run its course' – if you'll excuse the pun –
eliminating the toxins, but you do need to put back
fluids and balance the electrolytes in your body too!

Ingredients

1 serving
½ mango, peeled
1 pear, peeled and cored
1 banana, peeled
150 ml (3 ½ fl oz) rice milk
Pinch ground cinnamon

Method

Put the mango, pear and banana into
a blender/food processor with the
rice milk and whizz together. Serve
with a dusting of ground cinnamon.

Raspberry Relief

Raspberries are astringent and protect the gut from inflammation. They, like honey, have natural antibiotics too, helping to fight off infecting organisms in the gut.

Ingredients

1 serving

100 g (4 oz) raspberries – a few saved for garnish

2 large tbsp natural, live yoghurt

1–2 tsp honey

2 tbsp milk

Method

Put all the ingredients into a blender/food processor and whizz together. Pour into a glass, garnish with the reserved raspberries and sip slowly.

Papaya and Almond Dream

Diverticulitis is fast affecting a growing number of people in the west because of diets rich in highly processed foods, low in fibre and too many caffeinated drinks. A luscious combination of laxative and soothing fruits and anti-inflammatory rice milk can help, as will increasing the amount of exercise.

Ingredients

1 serving

6 fresh or 4 dried apricots (re-hydrate by cooking them in a little water until plump, cool and drain)

¼ papaya, peeled and de-seeded

300 ml (½ pint) rice milk

2 tsp ground almonds

Pinch of ground or fresh grated ginger

Method

Place all the ingredients in a blender/food processor and whizz together until smooth. Pour into a glass and sprinkle with a little ginger.

Pear and Melon

Both pears and melons are cooling and soothing in the digestive tract.
They help to relieve inflammation and keep the bowels regular.

Ingredients

1 serving

½ yellow melon, peeled and
de-seeded

2 pears, peeled and cored

Splash of coconut milk (optional)

Method

Place the pears and melon flesh in a food
processor/blend and whizz together. If you like,
add a splash of coconut milk. Serve in a glass.

Papaya and Coconut

IBS is becoming an increasingly common disease: it may be related to diet, stress, food intolerance or excessive levels of candida in the gut. Coconut milk is rich in vitamin B to strengthen the nerves; limes and honey keep the balance of good bacteria in the gut at an optimum level, while the sweet papaya enhances digestion and soothes the gut.

Ingredients

1 serving
papaya, peeled and de-seeded
Juice of 1 lime
1 tsp honey
300 ml (½ pint) coconut milk
Slice of lime to garnish

Method

Blend the papaya, lime juice, coconut milk and honey in a blender/food processor. Pour into a glass and garnish with a slice of lime.

Ruskie

Sitting comfortably? One-third of people in the west suffer from piles (haemorrhoids). The best cure is always prevention: plenty of fibre, plenty of exercise and avoid getting constipated. Live yoghurt helps if you are predisposed to constipation, while beetroot cleanses the liver and stimulates the bowels into action. (A friend from St. Petersburg swears by this – especially with a shot of vodka on the side!)

Ingredients

1 serving

½ small beetroot

2 celery stalks

150 ml (½ fl oz) natural, live yoghurt

1 spring onion, chopped

Fresh mint to garnish

Method

Wash, chop and juice the beetroot and the celery. Combine with the natural yoghurt, stirring well. Garnish with a little chopped spring onion and the fresh mint sprig.

Avocado Smoothie

Packed with energy and immune-boosting properties that help increase antibody production, avocados help keep your hair, mucus membranes, sweat glands, nerves and muscles in peak condition. As well as being anticancer and antioxidant, avocados are also believed to be antifungal.

Ingredients

1 serving

1 avocado, peeled and chopped

1 pear, peeled and cored

½ grapefruit, squeezed or juiced

1 teaspoon fresh ginger, finely chopped

100 ml (4 fl oz) soya milk

4 tbsp natural, live yoghurt

Method

Place all the ingredients into a blender/food processor and whizz together until smooth. Pour into a glass and serve straight away.

Carrot and Parsley

A delicious remedy for cystitis: carrots soothe and are also antiseptic, helping to combat infection. Parsley is also highly antiseptic, and, like carrots, is diuretic – which makes them a particularly dynamic duo. Drink this twice daily to relieve the symptoms of cystitis.

Ingredients

1 serving
4 carrots
6 sprigs fresh parsley

Method

Juice the carrots and the parsley.
Blend the juices together.

Cranberry Spritzer

With cystitis, prevention is the best course of action. Cranberry juice prevents bacteria from sticking to the walls of the urinary tract, so they can be easily 'swept' out of the system before they have a chance to cause infection.

Ingredients

1 serving

200 g (7 oz) cranberries, or 100 ml (3 ½ fl oz) cranberry juice

100 ml (3 ½ fl oz) sparkling mineral water

1 slice of lemon or lime

Method

Juice the cranberries and pour into a glass – over ice is nice. Top with sparkling mineral water and decorate with a slice of lime or lemon.

Cranberry Cure

A lovely, refreshing drink – even if you don't suffer from cystitis! Watermelon – or a tea made by simmering its seeds in hot water for 30 minutes – has long been used as a natural remedy for bladder – and kidney – troubles.

Ingredients

1 serving

200 g (7 oz) cranberries, or 100 ml (3 ½ fl oz) cranberry juice

1 large slice/wedge of watermelon

Method

Wash the cranberries and the water melon – you can juice the skin and the seeds as well, or peel and de-seed if you prefer. Combine the juices in a glass, admire the colour and enjoy.

Watermelon Waterfall

Since 95% of the nutrients are in the rind, it's a shame to cut it off the watermelon! In it you'll find chlorophyll, vitamin A, protein, potassium, zinc, iodine, nucleic acids and enzymes to aid digestion and cleanse the body. Grapes inhibit the action of allergens, viruses and carcinogens and are scavengers of free radicals. These juicy fruits are ideal 'cleaners' of the skin, liver, kidneys and bowels.

Ingredients

1 serving

150 g (5 oz) red grapes – a few kept aside to garnish

1 large slice/wedge watermelon

Method

Rinse the grapes, wash the rind of the melon if you are going to juice it too – and the seeds! Juice the grapes and then the watermelon. Combine the juices in a glass and garnish with a couple of grapes to nibble on.

Cranberry Grape

Another delightful way to keep bladder infections at bay – and to enjoy the goodness of freshly juiced fruit.

Ingredients

1 serving
2 apples
100 g (3 ½ oz) grapes
50 g (1 ¾ oz) cranberries
1 slice of lemon or lime

Method

Rinse, remove the stalks and juice the grapes. Rinse and juice the cranberries. Wash the apples, cut into chunks and juice. Combine the juices in a glass – over ice if you wish – and garnish with the slice of lemon or lime – or both if you like!

Sweet Lassi

A traditional Indian drink that is not only refreshing but also helps deal with flatulence. The live, natural yoghurt is especially beneficial for restoring the balance of 'good bacteria' in the gut. Cardamom and cinnamon stimulate the flow of digestive juices and help relieve tension throughout the digestive tract.

Ingredients

1 serving

124 ml (4 fl oz) natural, live yoghurt

75 ml (⅛ pint) rose water

1 teaspoon honey

Pinch ground cardamom

Pinch ground cinnamon

Method

Simply combine all the ingredients together, stirring well, and serve in a glass. Sip slowly.

Spring Cleaners

There comes a moment in everyone's life when it feels like the time to make changes: a new job or complete career change, a house move, or even shedding a few pounds because we're not happy with the way we look and feel. Most of the times we decide to make changes are when things are not going quite as well as we had hoped, or when we've had a disaster – at work, in a relationship, or at home – if the roof starts to leak! Chances are, the struggle to 'make things better' or to cope with an emergency will have taken its toll on our bodies, depleting them of energy reserves, stripping them of vital vitamins and minerals and leaving us open to infections.

If we want the changes we make to our lives to be a success, then not only do we need to think through all the alternatives available to us, we really do need to be fit and well to tackle the new challenges that await us.

When we get ill and are confined to our beds, we have ample time to think and plan our 'new life', but we mustn't overlook the fact that our bodies are going to need some sustained 'TLC' in the recovery period. If you're planning a major change in your life – whether it's retraining for a new career or taking up a new sport or activity – first get your body in shape! If you were doing a spring clean of your home, you'd have to find the time, get your dusters and vacuum cleaner at the ready, and clear the decks for action in order to do the job properly – and successfully. If you're going to 'spring clean' your body, you need to do exactly the same!

Detoxification – or detoxing as it has become popularly known in recent years – is the process of getting rid of waste and built-up stores of toxins in your body. The harmful substances or toxins are in the foods we eat on a regular basis, especially if our diet is rich in processed and highly refined foods, fast foods and junk foods full of

The properties of fruits and vegetables can help in 'spring cleaning'.

preservatives, artificial flavours, colours and sweeteners. These foods are the equivalents of 'dust-bunnies' – those grey, unhealthy bundles of fluff that you can find under your bed! We need to sweep up and dispose of them so they don't take over the bedroom! The same principle is true of toxins in the body.

A seasonal clean-out of the body does not mean pain or giving up eating! When you spring clean your home you don't throw away all your furniture, but maybe dispose of some old things and replace them with bright new ones! When you detox you cut out the processed foods as well as the caffeine, alcohol, candies and ideally the cigarettes that have been adding an extra burden to your body, but most importantly, you replace them with fresh natural foods that will boost your energy (in the way that caffeine has kept you awake!), lift your

Try a 'Flush-a-bye (p247) as an internal cleanser.

spirits (like a glass of champagne!) satisfy your cravings for something sweet (like the candies) and instead of lungfuls of carcinogenic smoke, try breathing some fresh air, or smelling the aromas of fresh apples, or cherries, or melons instead!

Like a good clean up around the house, a detox needs planning and timing: you need to set aside the time to do it. A one-day detox only takes a little will power and is a great way to start the process. You can extend the detox to a weekend later on, and then a week once you've got used to the idea and found out more about cleansing and nourishing your body.

Tropical fruits are not only delicious, they are packed full of enzymes too.

A one day detox when you only drink juices is pretty easy to do – it's also easy on the body because for only 24 hours it has to deal with nothing except the goodness in the juices, which give it the 'space' and energy to get on and get rid of the toxins that have built up in your system. On a one day detox, you'll need at least six glasses of juice PLUS plenty of water. You'll need to drink at least eight 8 fl oz glasses of water – although some can be in the form of herbal teas – as juice alone doesn't have enough.

Look in your diary, find a day that is right for you, then take a look at the recipes suggested. Choose the ingredients and flavours you like – detox is not a punishment! – then go out and buy your ingredients. Treat yourself to organic produce and mineral water. Take your time to select the finest fruits and vegetables: admire the colour, smell their scents, feel their ripeness, think of their homelands and their journey to you! Fall in love with fruit – and vegetables.

Take the day nice and easy – don't start running and jumping around – just relax. A detox

Juices are ideal for a gentle Detox day.

is more than just a physical spring clean: for thousands of years 'fasts' have been used as a pathway to spiritual enlightenment – and holiness. You may indeed find that your senses and awareness become more heightened, and that you feel physically lighter and mentally calmed.

Start the day with a yoghurt smoothie full of energy and lactobacillus to help maintain a healthy balance of

A yoghurt smoothie will set you up for the day.

bacteria in the gut. Have lunch when you are ready for it – not because the clock says it's time! Take your time, sip your drink, then relax some more – a good book, a video, or even a little snooze if you feel drowsy. When the hunger pangs set in again, don't give in to a takeaway. Instead indulge in a really long juice and end the day with a calming herbal tea just before bed to ensure a good night's sleep.

The next day when you awake, your body is going to be grumbling away noisily asking for food. Yes, you'll awake more peckish than usual – and most likely, a little earlier than normal – so take this extra time to prepare yourself a balanced breakfast: some yoghurt, fruit, a slice of wholemeal toast and a herbal tea or juice perhaps. Go on, surprise yourself at how very 'civilised' your palate and taste buds have become in just one day! Once you've got the hang of detoxing with your gentle 'one day' programme, you may find that you want to do it again, and for a longer period. Longer detoxes need careful planning, so it's a good idea to read about the process – and all the other things that can be integrated into a detox – such as massage, exercise and relaxation therapies, as well as beauty regimes.

There are a number of excellent books available to help you plan – and achieve – your goals, so do some research first, and discover the benefits you can gain from a detox programme.

It is vital too that if you are ill or suffer from any medical condition you consult a medically qualified practitioner before you embark on any longer regime.

Tickle your tastebuds with exciting flavours.

Warning

Children, the elderly, pregnant and nursing mothers or anyone with an existing medical condition should not consider a detox or juice fast. If you are ill, have or suspect you may have an allergy or food intolerance, you need to consult a doctor. The recipes suggested are NOT substitutes for medical advice or prescribed medicines. Never 'fast' for more than 24 hours at a time without medical supervision.

Ginger Grapes

Start the day with a cleansing tonic for your insides. Grapes are one of the world's oldest cultivated plants. Nutritionally they contain vitamins A, B-complex and C, and the minerals potassium and calcium. High in natural sugars, they will put a spring in your step.

Ingredients

1 serving

About 25 red grapes – keep a couple for garnish

5 cm (2 in) slice fresh ginger, peeled

1 lemon, peeled

100 ml (3 ½ fl oz) sparkling or still mineral water

Sprig of mint

Method

Rinse the grapes, peel and chop the lemon and peel the ginger. Juice the ingredients, combine in a glass and top with mineral water. Garnish with a sprig of mint and a few grapes. You can make this in a blender/food processor too, but it's worth grating the ginger first.

Pink Kiwi

This is like a 'kiwi colada' – but without the booze! It's really refreshing and full of vitamins – kiwis contain twice the vitamin C of oranges and have only around 45 calories per fruit – minerals like potassium (a lack of which can lead to depression) and enzymes such as papayin which 'digests' proteins.

Ingredients

1 serving

½ papaya, peeled and de-seeded

2 kiwi fruits, peeled if you prefer

75 g (about 2 oz) cherries, de-stoned

1 pear, cut into chunks

Crushed ice

Soda water, or sparkling mineral water

Method

Put the kiwis and papaya, cherries and pear in a blender/food processor and whizz until smooth. Add a splash of mineral water or soda water to taste. Crush some ice, add to a glass and pour the fruit puree over the ice. Garnish with a slice of kiwi and sip through a straw.

Dill-lightful

The lacy dill, whose name is derived from the old Norse word *dilla*, which means 'to lull', does have a mild soporific effect: in the 1800s dill seeds, known as 'meeting seeds', were given to children to chew on in church to keep them quiet! Cucumber, with its high water content is a terrific 'internal rinse', while tomatoes and carrots – full of vitamins C and E, betacarotene and potassium – are great detoxers.

Ingredients

1 serving

1 small bunch of dill

$^1/_2$ cucumber – a slice or two reserved for garnish – peeled if you wish

1 large tomato

1 carrot

Cayenne pepper or black pepper to taste

Method

Rinse and dry the dill and reserve a few sprigs for garnish. Strip the fronds from the stalks and finely chop the lacy leaves. Peel the cucumber if you wish – some folks say the peel makes them 'burp'! Juice the cucumber, carrot and tomato and blend with the chopped dill until smooth. Season to taste and pour into a glass garnished with a slice or two of cucumber and a sprig of dill.

Holiday

With lots of essential nutrients to 'feed' body – and spirit– bromelain in pineapple is a 'fat buster' and mango will provide you with your daily requirement of vitamin C, two-thirds of your vitamin A, half your vitamin E and almost a quarter of your fibre. They are wonderful foods for 'slimmers' as their natural sweetness means you won't want to snack on junk food as you prepare for your bikini!

Ingredients

1 serving

1 small banana

$^{1}/_{2}$ mango

$^{1}/_{4}$ pineapple

Tonic water or sparkling mineral water (optional)

Method

Peel the banana, mango and pineapple. In a blender/food processor, whizz all of the ingredients together. If the mix is a little too thick, dilute with tonic or sparkling mineral water. Pour into a glass, add a straw, a cocktail umbrella, a chunk of pineapple and dream of blue seas and palm fringed, white beaches.

Lettuce Milk

Because lettuce is 95% water and only 7 calories or so in an average serving, it's no surprise it's a weight-watchers standby. The ancient Egyptians and Romans knew a thing or two about lettuce and suspected that its surprisingly bitter lettuce juice was much more than water – and they were right! Surprisingly full of vitamin C, betacarotene, folic acid, lots of potassium and some calcium too, a little iodine and just a pinch or iron. Carotinoids detoxify the body, and there are more of these in the darker leaves – so eat – or drink–your greens!

Ingredients

1 serving

2 or 3 large lettuce leaves – the darkest green you can find

1 tbsp ground almonds

2 apples

1 tomato

100 ml (3 $\frac{1}{2}$ fl oz) buttermilk, or live natural yoghurt

$\frac{1}{2}$ lemon

Pinch of nutmeg

Method

Wash the apples, tomato and lettuce leaves and pat dry. Juice the tomato, lettuce leaves and apple and combine with the ground almonds and buttermilk, or live natural yoghurt. Wash the lemon and grate half the peel finely, then squeeze half of the juice into the mix. Pour into a glass and dust a little fresh nutmeg on the top. Decorate with a slice of lemon.

Four Fruit Energy

This is a terrific spring tonic – excellent for dispelling those winter blues and getting the sap rising!

Ingredients

1 serving

$^{1}/_{2}$ papaya

2 kiwis

1 orange

$^{1}/_{2}$ grapefruit – a pink one if possible!

Method

Peel the papaya and scoop out the seeds. Peel the kiwis and keep a slice or two for decoration. In a blender/food processor, whizz the papaya and kiwis together into a puree. Peel and juice the grapefruit and orange and combine the juices with the fruit puree. Blend together: if a little too thick, add a splash of mineral water. Pour into a glass and decorate with the kiwi – or a slice of orange/grapefruit

Apple Smoothie

Smoothies made with live natural yoghurt and fresh fruit juices are a great way to start the day – and you keep the balance of 'good bacteria' in your gut. Whether detoxing or weight-watching, it is vital that your body is nourished. You need to replace vital vitamins and minerals and energise your body to keep it working efficiently: a well maintained car is a reliable and fuel-efficient vehicle, but a broken down jalopy won't get you where you want!

Ingredients

1 serving

1 apple

2 oranges

100 ml (3 fl oz) natural live yoghurt (see recipe on page 49 to make your own)

10 small mint leaves, finely chopped

Method

Wash and juice the apple. Peel and juice the orange. Pour the yoghurt into a blender/food processor and add the juices. Whizz until smooth. Sprinkle with chopped mint leaves and garnish with a slice of orange if you like. If you want a longer drink, add a splash or two of chilled mineral water.

Strawberry Shake-up

These summer berries contain bromelain, which helps to 'digest' fat – that's why strawberries go so well with cream! Using yoghurt – which you can make yourself (see page 49) – gives a creamy, satisfying texture, so it's nice without being naughty! In summer, try this shake chilled, it's as nice as ice cream and it's full of goodness too!

Ingredients

1 serving

100 g (3 oz) strawberries

150 ml (3 ½ fl oz) natural live yoghurt

50 g (1 ½ oz) – about 8–10 – grapes (red or green)

1 orange

Method

Wash and hull the strawberries. Trying not to eat it, put one aside for garnish! You can either pass all the fruits through a juicer, or puree them in a blender/food processor. Add the juice/puree to the yoghurt and blend until smooth. Pour into a large glass, decorate with the strawberry and serve with a straw.

Cucumber-Melon

Melon contains betacarotene, folic acid and minerals, such as calcium, choline and magnesium, while cucumber is potassium rich. Both have diuretic properties and are great detoxers. By adding some natural, live yoghurt, this becomes quite a substantial drink.

Ingredients

1 serving

½ cucumber

½ cantaloupe melon

150 ml (3 ½ fl oz) natural, live yoghurt

2–3 sprigs of fresh dill

Seasoning to taste

Method

Wash the dill and strip the leaves from the stalks – save a sprig for garnish if you like. Chop up the rest of the dill very finely. Peel the cucumber, and de-seed and remove the flesh from the melon. In a blender/food processor, puree the cucumber and melon. Sprinkle in the dill, pour in the yoghurt and blend briefly until smooth. Season with pepper to taste. Pour into a tall glass, garnish with the dill and a slice of cucumber if you like, and enjoy.

Grapefruit and Pineapple Spritzer

Grapefruit has long been the weight-watchers fruit of choice – and oh! how people have punished themselves with half a yellow grapefruit for breakfast! The pinker the grapefruit the sweeter the taste – but you'll still get more than one and half times your daily vitamin C requirements, as well as potassium and pectin.

Ingredients

1 serving
¼ pineapple, peeled
1 pink grapefruit
Sparkling mineral water
Ice cubes (optional)

Method

Peel and juice the pineapple and grapefruit. Combine the juices in a tall glass – over ice if you like – and top with sparkling mineral water. Garnish with a slice of grapefruit if you like, add a straw and enjoy!

Radish-kohlrabi

Named by the Germans 'cabbage turnip' (kohl = cabbage, rabi = turnip), it resembles both in appearance and taste The small ones are best – big ones are usually a little tough and 'woody'. They contain notable amounts of vitamin C and calcium, while the leafy tops are high in vitamin A.

Ingredients

1 serving

3 radishes

¼ small kohlrabi

2 stalks of celery – one for a munchy garnish

100 ml (3 ½ fl oz) natural live yoghurt

Seasoning to taste

Method

Wash the radishes and celery, and wash and peel the kohlrabi. Chop the veggies into chunks – keeping a celery stalk for garnish – and juice them. Blend the juices with the yoghurt and season with salt – try a pinch of celery salt! – and pepper to taste. Pour into a glass and serve with a celery stalk. You can also use a blender/food processor: chop the veggies finely and puree them, then pass the puree through a fine sieve. Mix with the yoghurt and serve.

Grape Cooler

A lovely colour, a terrific dry taste, and a real tonic for the body and mind, especially after cooling down from a little exercise.

Ingredients

1 serving
100 g (3 ½ oz) red grapes
200 g (7 oz) cranberries
1 lime
Sparkling mineral water
Ice

Method

Peel the lime – keep a slice or two for garnish – and juice it. If you can resist eating them, keep a couple of grapes and cranberries aside too! Juice the grapes and cranberries. Pour all the juices over ice cubes in a glass and top with sparkling water. Garnish with the reserved fruit. Add a straw and a swizzle stick.

Grapefruit and Apple Tonic

Yellow grapefruits can be a little sharp but they are so good for you. In this recipe, their goodness shines through, but their sharpness is blunted somewhat by the addition of sweet apples. This makes a lovely morning drink: the natural sugars give you an energy 'high' without the 'low' afterwards!

Ingredients

1 serving
1 apple
1 grapefruit

Method

Wash the apple, chop into chunks and juice. Peel the grapefruit and juice it. Combine the juices in a glass and feel yourself tingle! If you like a more substantial breakfast drink, make it into a smoothie with 150 ml (5 fl oz) of natural, live yoghurt.

Flush-a-bye

Cranberries and melon – a yellow melon or watermelon – and cucumber make a great cooling and invigorating drink that also nourishes and cleanses.

Ingredients

1 serving

200 g (7 oz) cranberries

1 good thick slice of watermelon or ¼ yellow melon

250 g (8 oz) cucumber

A stick or a couple of slices of cucumber for garnish

Method

Wash the cranberries and juice them. Wash – and peel if you like – the cucumber and juice it. Scoop the flesh – along with the seeds as they are edible – from the melon and juice this. If you use a watermelon, you can juice the skin as well! Combine the juices in a glass and garnish with the cucumber stick or slices.

Apple and Apricot Smoothie

A meal in itself: apricots are high in fibre and low in calories but satisfy that urge for something sweet! Apples aid digestion and absorption and have the ability to 'dampen' the appetite – always a bonus when you're keeping one eye on the weighing scales!

Ingredients

1 serving

Six fresh apricots (or 4–5 dried apricots)

2 apples

100 ml (3 ½ fl oz) live natural yoghurt

A little freshly grated nutmeg

Method

Wash and de-stone the apricots then juice. (If using dried apricots, rehydrate them by covering with just enough water in a saucepan and heating slowly. When 'plump', allow to cool and drain.) Juice or puree them in a blender/food processor. Wash and chop the apples and either juice or puree in a blender/food processor. Mix the juices or fruit purees with the yoghurt in a blender/food processor until smooth. Pour into a glass and dust with a little grated nutmeg.

Thai Tango

An exotic combination of tropical fruits, this drink is great for 'reduction' but is also very satisfying – a great way to get those taste buds dancing! The papaya is packed with vitamin C, betacarotene and enzymes to aid digestion. Pears have a diuretic action to help eliminate toxins and are full of fibre and the lime helps to clear excess fluids from the body. In all, it's a 'gym in a glass'!

Ingredients

1 serving

½ papaya, peeled and de-seeded

1 lime, juiced – keep a slice for garnish

2 pears

150 ml (5 fl oz) rice milk

Pinch ground ginger

Ice cubes (optional)

Method

Cut the papaya flesh into chunks and puree with the juice of the lime in a blender/food processor. Cut the pears into chunks, add these to the mix and puree them too. Pour in the rice milk and whizz together until smooth. Pour over ice cubes for a long refreshing drink. Dust with a pinch of ground ginger and garnish with a slice or two of lime.

Citron and Grape Presse

This is so simple to make – and you can have it hot or cold. Refreshing and cleansing, this is a perfect way to start your day.

Ingredients

1 serving

1 lemon, with a slice reserved for garnish

100g (3 ½ oz) green grapes – a few reserved for garnish

Ice cubes (optional)

Chilled mineral water (still or sparkling) or hot water to make up to 200 ml (7 fl oz)

Method

Juice the lemons and the grapes. Pour into an ice filled glass and top up with chilled mineral water. Omit the ice cubes and use a heatproof glass if adding hot water. Garnish with a few grapes and a slice of lemon.

Waterfall

Grapes, pears and melon are all highly nutritious, rich in vitamins and minerals and, as the name of this drink suggests, are great for 'strengthening' the action of the kidneys! You can replace the grapes with apples if you like, it's still great!

Ingredients

1 serving
150g (5 oz) grapes (or 2 apples)
2 pears
¼ yellow melon
Ice cubes (optional)
Ground ginger to garnish

Method

Juice the grapes, pears and melon (you can juice the skin and pips too!) and combine in a glass, over ice if you like, Garnish with a few grapes and a dusting of ground ginger.

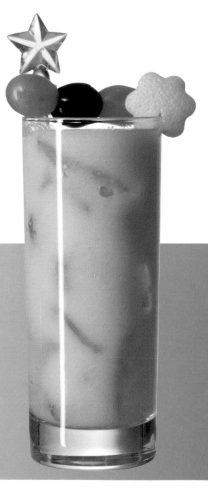

Liquid Lunch

Watching your weight doesn't mean punishing your body by denying it nourishment and goodness. Nor does it mean starving yourself! You need energy, vitamins, minerals and fibre without the empty calories of highly processed or 'junk food'. This 'meal in a glass' will provide you with nourishment and satisfy hunger. If you want a little more sweetness, add an orange into the mix.

Ingredients

1 serving

2 carrots
½ cucumber
2 stalks celery
½ small beetroot
1 orange (optional)

Method

Wash the veggies and juice the beetroot, followed by the carrots, then the celery and then the cucumber. (If you want to add an orange, then juice this too!) Combine the juices in a glass and garnish with a carrot stick, a celery stalk and a wedge of orange – they not only look nice but you can give your jaws a 'workout' too!

Melon Marvel

If you are still a little peckish at the end of the day, don't give in to salty snacks. Instead go for this substantial juice.

Ingredients

1 serving
½ yellow melon
2 pears
2 cm (¾ in) fresh ginger
Sprig of lemon balm or mint

Method

Remove the flesh from the melon, chop up the pears and peel and chop the ginger. Juice the fruits in the following order: pears, ginger and melon. Mix the juices in a glass and garnish with a sprig of lemon balm or mint. Sip slowly.

Index

Bibliography

Friedrich Bohlmann *Energy Drinks* Gaia Books, 1999

Rose Elliot and Carlo de Paoli *Kitchen Pharmacy* Orion, 1991

Kirsten Hartvig *Eat For Immunity* Duncan Baird, 2002

Kirsten Hartvig and Nick Rowley *Energy Juices,* Duncan Baird, 2001

Patrick Holford *The Optimum Nutrition Bible* Piatkus, 1997

Leslie Kenton *The Raw Energy Bible,* Vermillion, 1998

Anne McIntyre *Healing Drinks* Gaia Books, 1999

Anne McIntyre *Herbs for Common Ailments* Gaia, 1999

Judith Millidge *The Handbook of Smoothies and Juicing,* Silverdale Books, 2003

Evelyn Roehl *Whole Food Facts* Healing Arts Press, 1996

Jane Sen *The Healing Foods Cookbook* Thorsons, 1996

Michael van Straten *Foods for Mind and Body,* Thorsons, 1997

Michael van Straten *Superjuice* Mitchell Beazley, 1999

Caroline Wheater *Juicing For Health* Thorsons, 1993

Rebecca Wood *The Whole Foods Encyclopedia* Prentice Hall, 1988

Charmaine Yabsley and Amanada Cross *Miracle Juices,* Hamlyn, 2001

Charmaine Yabsley and Amanada Cross *Juices and Smoothies,* Hamlyn, 2003